10 Days to
Multiplication Mastery
Student Workbook

Original book written by: Marion W. Stuart

Editors: Cindy Barden and Linda Armstrong

Cover Design: R. Matthew Stuart

Illustrations: Nancee J. McClure

Book Design: Good Neighbor Press, Inc.

Copyright © 2008 Learning Wrap-Ups, Inc.

First Printing

Learning Wrap-Ups, Inc.
1660 W. Gordon Avenue #4
Layton, UT 84041

ISBN: 1-59204-113-2

ISBN 13: 978-1-59204-113-8

Table of Contents

10 Days to Multiplication Mastery Student Workbook

Wouldn't it be great if you could master the multiplication tables in 10 days? With Learning Wrap-Ups™ and this workbook, you can!

There are 2 great secrets to multiplication mastery.

Secret 1: The Commutative Property of Multiplication

The numbers (factors) in a multiplication number sentence (equation) may be put in any order. The answer (product) will be the same.

Example:

$A \times B = C$ $(3 \times 5 = 15)$

$B \times A = C$ $(5 \times 3 = 15)$

Secret 2: Practice, Practice, Practice

Don't worry! Learning Wrap-Ups™ and the activity pages in this book will make practicing times tables easy and fun. The Wrap-Ups™ are your best friends in this program. Take some time to learn to use them.

Directions for using the Wrap-Ups

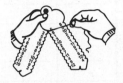

1. Hold the bundle of wrap-ups at the top of the key and choose the board you want to wrap.

2. Begin with the string next to the first number on the left. Read the large number in the center and multiply (example 3×1). Find the answer on the right side of the key. Then, draw the string around the back to the next number on the left. Continue the process from top to bottom until all numbers have been matched.

3. As you wrap the keys, say the problems and answers aloud. Hearing the facts will help you learn them faster.

4. When finished, slip the string into the notch at the bottom of the key. See if the string lines match the raised lines on the back of the key. If the lines match, the key is wrapped correctly. If the lines do not match, check your answers and wrap the key again, correctly.

5. Always wrap as fast as you can.

The Goal

When you finish this workbook, you will be able to complete each of the 10 Wrap-Ups™ in 30 seconds or less! You will surprise yourself by completing the final written test in record time.

Facts I've Learned

As you complete the daily exercises, write the answer to each problem you have learned down the column, then write the answers for the commutative partners across each row. Choose a different color for each day and lightly color the problems you have mastered.

1 ×1	1 ×2	1 ×3	1 ×4	1 ×5	1 ×6	1 ×7	1 ×8	1 ×9	1 ×10	1 ×11	1 ×12
2 ×1	2 ×2	2 ×3	2 ×4	2 ×5	2 ×6	2 ×7	2 ×8	2 ×9	2 ×10	2 ×11	2 ×12
3 ×1	3 ×2	3 ×3	3 ×4	3 ×5	3 ×6	3 ×7	3 ×8	3 ×9	3 ×10	3 ×11	3 ×12
4 ×1	4 ×2	4 ×3	4 ×4	4 ×5	4 ×6	4 ×7	4 ×8	4 ×9	4 ×10	4 ×11	4 ×12
5 ×1	5 ×2	5 ×3	5 ×4	5 ×5	5 ×6	5 ×7	5 ×8	5 ×9	5 ×10	5 ×11	5 ×12
6 ×1	6 ×2	6 ×3	6 ×4	6 ×5	6 ×6	6 ×7	6 ×8	6 ×9	6 ×10	6 ×11	6 ×12
7 ×1	7 ×2	7 ×3	7 ×4	7 ×5	7 ×6	7 ×7	7 ×8	7 ×9	7 ×10	7 ×11	7 ×12
8 ×1	8 ×2	8 ×3	8 ×4	8 ×5	8 ×6	8 ×7	8 ×8	8 ×9	8 ×10	8 ×11	8 ×12
9 ×1	9 ×2	9 ×3	9 ×4	9 ×5	9 ×6	9 ×7	9 ×8	9 ×9	9 ×10	9 ×11	9 ×12
10 ×1	10 ×2	10 ×3	10 ×4	10 ×5	10 ×6	10 ×7	10 ×8	10 ×9	10 ×10	10 ×11	10 ×12
11 ×1	11 ×2	11 ×3	11 ×4	11 ×5	11 ×6	11 ×7	11 ×8	11 ×9	11 ×10	11 ×11	11 ×12
12 ×1	12 ×2	12 ×3	12 ×4	12 ×5	12 ×6	12 ×7	12 ×8	12 ×9	12 ×10	12 ×11	12 ×12

Day 1: 1s and 2s

Day 2: 10s and 3s

Day 3: 11s

Day 4: 4s

Day 5: 5s and Perfect Squares

Day 6: 6s

Day 7: 7s and 9s

Day 8: 8s

Day 9: Review

Day 10: Review/Celebrate

Example of how to color.

My Wrap-Ups Journal

Learning a skill is like taking a car trip. It can be very exciting. It can also be frustrating or disappointing. That is why there is a Wrap-Up™ journal at the end of this book. After finishing each day's work, take a few minutes to write about your experience.

You can write a sentence about something you learned. You can explain, in your own words, how you solved a problem. You can write about someone who helped you. You can even write about how you feel. Later, when you are a multiplication master, you will enjoy reading this record of your progress.

My Multiplication Glossary

Mathematicians use special words to describe number sentences and operations. The special terms used in *10 Days to Multiplication Mastery* are *product, factor, commutative property of multiplication, equation, perfect square, digit, column row,* and *sum.* You can review new terms in the glossary on page 60.

Use these terms to explain your work in class and your exercises at home. You will soon see why mathematicians like them. A carpenter would not try to drive a nail with pencil. He would use a hammer because it is the right tool for the job. These words are the right tools for talking about math.

Multiply by 0

> **Remember!**
> - **Zero multiplied by any number is always zero.**
> - **Any number multiplied by zero is always zero.**

Multiply.

1. $\begin{array}{r} 6 \\ \times\,0 \\ \hline \end{array}$
2. $\begin{array}{r} 0 \\ \times\,4 \\ \hline \end{array}$

3. $\begin{array}{r} 0 \\ \times\,9 \\ \hline \end{array}$
4. $\begin{array}{r} 5 \\ \times\,0 \\ \hline \end{array}$

5. $\begin{array}{r} 8 \\ \times\,0 \\ \hline \end{array}$
6. $\begin{array}{r} 0 \\ \times\,7 \\ \hline \end{array}$

The same rule applies to large numbers.

Multiply.

7. $99 \times 0 =$ _____
8. $549 \times 0 =$ _____
9. $0 \times 58 =$ _____
10. $0 \times 351 =$ _____

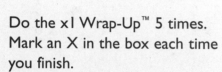

Multiply by 1

Remember!

★ 1 times any number equals that number.

●●●●   1 row of 4 dots
            1 x 4 = 4

★ Any number times 1 equals that number.

●
●   4 dots in 1 column
●   4 x 1 = 4
●

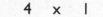
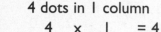

Do the x1 Wrap-Up™ 5 times.
Mark an X in the box each time
you finish.

rows:
go across like seats
in a theater.

columns:
go up and down
like pillars holding
up an overpass.

★ **Meet your Goal**
Do the x1 Wrap-Up™
until you meet
your goal.

Multiply.

1 x 2	2 x 1	2 x 1	1 x 2
3 x 1	1 x 3	4 x 1	1 x 4
5 x 1	1 x 5	6 x 1	1 x 6
7 x 1	1 x 7	8 x 1	1 x 8
9 x 1	1 x 9	10 x 1	1 x 10
11 x 1	1 x 11	12 x 1	1 x 12

You know all the answers for x1. Now do the x1
Wrap-Up™ as fast as you can. Practice until you can
reach your goal.

1 minute	45 seconds	30 seconds	20 seconds	15 seconds	10 seconds
Getting started!	First goal. Keep going!	Champ!	Super Champ!	Awesome!	Next to impossible!

Day 1   Wrap-Ups and Rapid Writing

1. Write the answers to the problems in the first column as fast as you can.

2. Do the x1 Learning Wrap-Up™ until you meet your goal. Mark a box in the Keeping Track section each time you complete the Wrap-Up™.

3. Write the answers to the second and third columns as fast as you can.

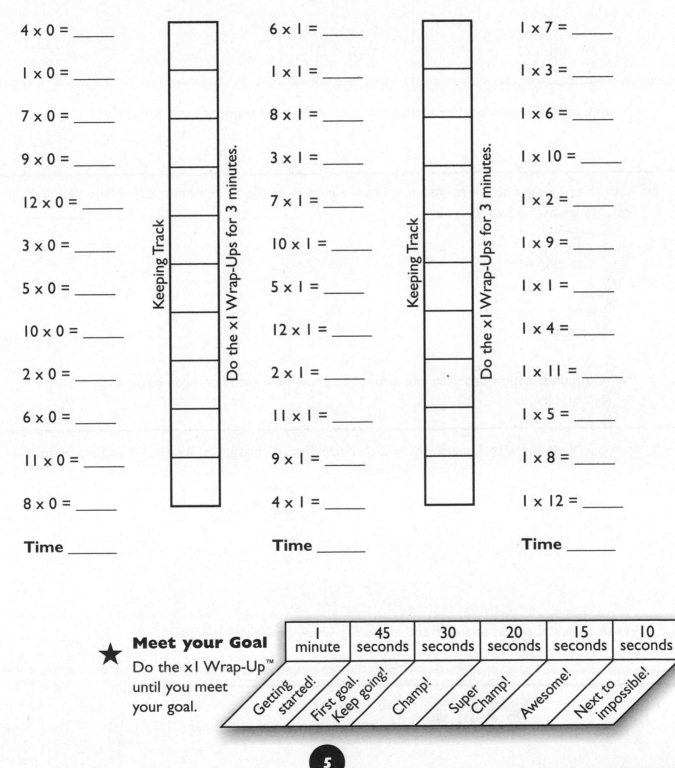

4 x 0 = _____

1 x 0 = _____

7 x 0 = _____

9 x 0 = _____

12 x 0 = _____

3 x 0 = _____

5 x 0 = _____

10 x 0 = _____

2 x 0 = _____

6 x 0 = _____

11 x 0 = _____

8 x 0 = _____

Time _____

Keeping Track

Do the x1 Wrap-Ups for 3 minutes.

6 x 1 = _____

1 x 1 = _____

8 x 1 = _____

3 x 1 = _____

7 x 1 = _____

10 x 1 = _____

5 x 1 = _____

12 x 1 = _____

2 x 1 = _____

11 x 1 = _____

9 x 1 = _____

4 x 1 = _____

Time _____

Keeping Track

Do the x1 Wrap-Ups for 3 minutes.

1 x 7 = _____

1 x 3 = _____

1 x 6 = _____

1 x 10 = _____

1 x 2 = _____

1 x 9 = _____

1 x 1 = _____

1 x 4 = _____

1 x 11 = _____

1 x 5 = _____

1 x 8 = _____

1 x 12 = _____

Time _____

★ **Meet your Goal**
Do the x1 Wrap-Up™ until you meet your goal.

1 minute	45 seconds	30 seconds	20 seconds	15 seconds	10 seconds
Getting started!	First goal. Keep going!	Champ!	Super Champ!	Awesome!	Next to impossible!

5

Read each problem. Follow the directions.

---

1. Justin had 6 sacks. Each sack had 1 orange. Draw a picture of his sacks and oranges. The first sack is drawn for you.

Write a multiplication problem and answer to show how many oranges Justin had.

---

2. Kathy had 1 box with 6 oranges in it. Draw a picture of the oranges in the box. The box and the first orange are drawn for you.

Write a multiplication problem and answer to show now many oranges Kathy had.

---

3. Josh had 8 circles with 1 macaroni in each circle. Draw a picture of his circles and macaroni.

Write a multiplication problem and answer to show how many pieces of macaroni Josh had in all.

 You've mastered the 1s. You have **learned 23 facts**. Color in the chart on page 2.

6

Day 1

Multiply by 2
Concept & Commutative

Think About It!

$$\begin{array}{r} 2 \\ \times\,4 \\ \hline 8 \end{array}$$

2 buttons with 4 holes = _____ holes.

or

$$\begin{array}{r} 4 \\ \times\,2 \\ \hline 8 \end{array}$$

4 buttons with 2 holes = _____ holes.

$$\begin{array}{r} 2 \\ \times\,6 \\ \hline 12 \end{array}$$

2 jars with 6 bugs in each = _____ bugs.

or

$$\begin{array}{r} 6 \\ \times\,2 \\ \hline 12 \end{array}$$

6 jars with 2 bugs in each = _____ bugs.

Multiply.

1 ×2	2 ×1	2 ×2	2 ×2
3 ×2	2 ×3	4 ×2	2 ×4
5 ×2	2 ×5	6 ×2	2 ×6
7 ×2	2 ×7	8 ×2	2 ×8
9 ×2	2 ×9	10 ×2	2 ×10
11 ×2	2 ×11	12 ×2	2 ×12

Write all the 2 times tables and their commutative partners.

2 x 1 = 2   1 x 2 = 2

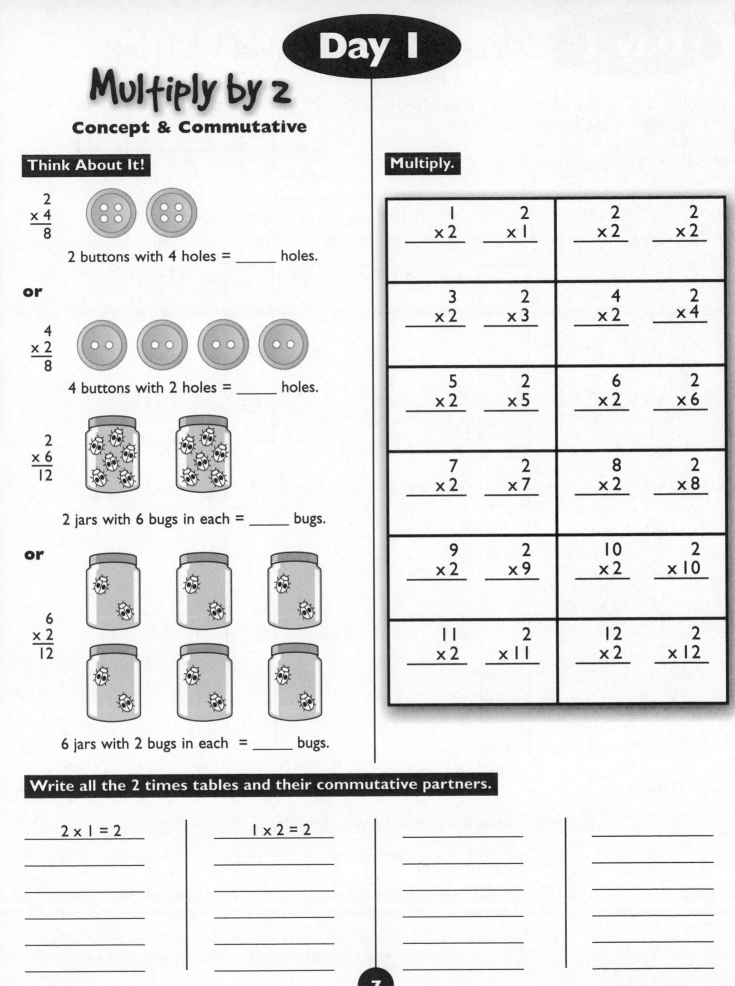

7

Day 1 Wrap-Ups and Rapid Writing

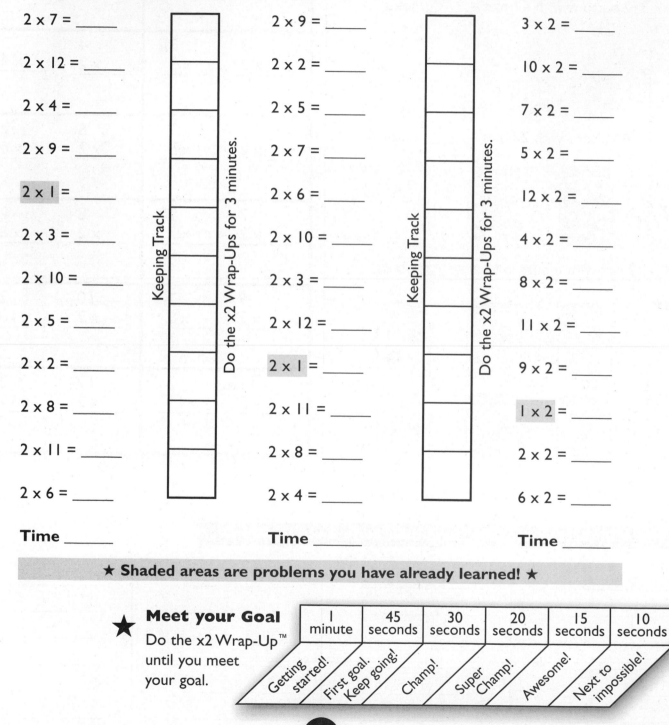

Do the x2 Wrap-Up™ 5 times. Mark an X in the box each time you finish.

1. Write the answers to the problems in the first column as fast as you can.
2. Do the x2 Learning Wrap-Up™ until you meet your goal. Mark a box in the Keeping Track section each time you complete the Wrap-Up™.
3. Write the answers to the second and third columns as fast as you can.

2 x 7 = _____

2 x 12 = _____

2 x 4 = _____

2 x 9 = _____

2 x 1 = _____

2 x 3 = _____

2 x 10 = _____

2 x 5 = _____

2 x 2 = _____

2 x 8 = _____

2 x 11 = _____

2 x 6 = _____

Time _____

Keeping Track

Do the x2 Wrap-Ups for 3 minutes.

2 x 9 = _____

2 x 2 = _____

2 x 5 = _____

2 x 7 = _____

2 x 6 = _____

2 x 10 = _____

2 x 3 = _____

2 x 12 = _____

2 x 1 = _____

2 x 11 = _____

2 x 8 = _____

2 x 4 = _____

Time _____

Keeping Track

Do the x2 Wrap-Ups for 3 minutes.

3 x 2 = _____

10 x 2 = _____

7 x 2 = _____

5 x 2 = _____

12 x 2 = _____

4 x 2 = _____

8 x 2 = _____

11 x 2 = _____

9 x 2 = _____

1 x 2 = _____

2 x 2 = _____

6 x 2 = _____

Time _____

★ Shaded areas are problems you have already learned! ★

★ **Meet your Goal**
Do the x2 Wrap-Up™ until you meet your goal.

1 minute	45 seconds	30 seconds	20 seconds	15 seconds	10 seconds
Getting started!	First goal. Keep going!	Champ!	Super Champ!	Awesome!	Next to impossible!

Day 1 Story Problems

Read each problem. Follow the directions.

---

1. Chris had 5 small candy bars. Each candy bar had 2 sections. Draw a picture to show how many sections of candy bars Chris had.

Write a multiplication problem to show how many sections of candy bars Chris had.

---

2. Andrea had 2 large candy bars. She cut each candy bar into 5 sections. Draw a picture to show how many sections Andrea had.

Write a multiplication problem to show how many sections of candy bars Andrea had.

---

3. The 7 families on Greg's block each had 2 children. Draw a picture to show how many children live on Greg's block.

Write a multiplication problem to show how many children live on Greg's block.

 You've mastered the 2s. You have **learned 44 facts**. Color in the chart on page 2.

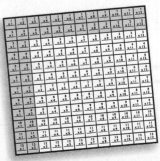

Day 1 Challenge and Review

Multiply. Shade in the bubble beside the correct product.

1

$0 \times 12 =$ _____

(a) 12   (b) 0

(c) 120   (d) None of these

2

$2 \times 8 =$ _____

(a) 10   (b) 12

(c) 16   (d) None of these

3

$1 \times 9 =$ _____

(a) 99   (b) 9

(c) 1   (d) None of these

4

Jan had 2 boxes of party treats. There were 5 party treats in each box. How many party treats did Jan have?

(a) 10 party treats

(b) 20 party treats

(c) 50 party treats

(d) None of these

5

Juana had 8 bags of crackers. There were 2 crackers in each bag. How many crackers did Juana have?

(a) 16 crackers

(b) 18 crackers

(c) 12 crackers

(d) None of these

6

Lee had 9 packages of light bulbs. There was 1 bulb in each package. How many light bulbs did Lee have?

(a) 18 bulbs

(b) 1 bulb

(c) 9 bulbs

(d) None of these

Day 2

Multiply by 10
Concept & Commutative

Think About It!

x1 and x10 are very similar. What do you notice?

1 x 7 = _____   10 x 7 = 70

4 x 1 = 4   4 x 10 = _____

1 x 3 = _____   10 x 3 = _____

Understanding

6 rows with
x 10 dots per row
60

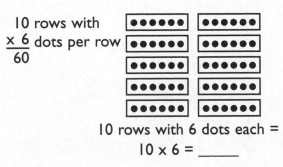

6 rows with 10 dots each =
6 x 10 = _____

or

10 rows with
x 6 dots per row
60

10 rows with 6 dots each =
10 x 6 = _____

Multiply.

10 x 1	1 x 10	10 x 2	2 x 10
10 x 3	3 x 10	10 x 4	4 x 10
10 x 5	5 x 10	10 x 6	6 x 10
10 x 7	7 x 10	10 x 8	8 x 10
10 x 9	9 x 10	10 x 10	10 x 10
10 x 11	11 x 10	10 x 12	12 x 10

Write all the 10 times tables and their commutative partners.

10 x 1 = 10   1 x 10 = 10

_____   _____   _____   _____

_____   _____   _____   _____

_____   _____   _____   _____

_____   _____   _____   _____

11

© Learning Wrap-Ups™, Inc. 2008

Do the x10 Wrap-Up™ 5 times. Mark an X in the box each time you finish.

1. Write the answers to the problems in the first column as fast as you can.
2. Do the x10 Learning Wrap-Up™ until you meet your goal. Mark a box in the Keeping Track section each time you complete the Wrap-Up™.
3. Write the answers to the second and third columns as fast as you can.

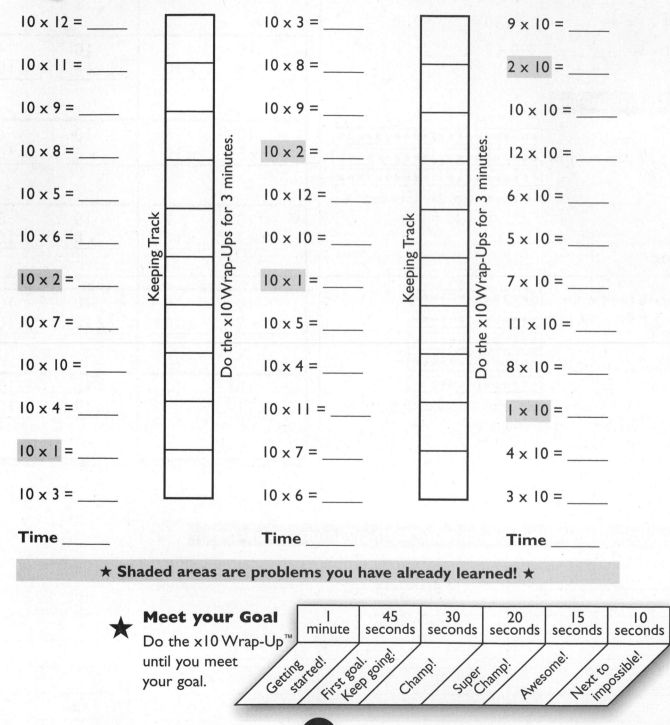

10 x 12 = _____	10 x 3 = _____	9 x 10 = _____
10 x 11 = _____	10 x 8 = _____	2 x 10 = _____
10 x 9 = _____	10 x 9 = _____	10 x 10 = _____
10 x 8 = _____	10 x 2 = _____	12 x 10 = _____
10 x 5 = _____	10 x 12 = _____	6 x 10 = _____
10 x 6 = _____	10 x 10 = _____	5 x 10 = _____
10 x 2 = _____	10 x 1 = _____	7 x 10 = _____
10 x 7 = _____	10 x 5 = _____	11 x 10 = _____
10 x 10 = _____	10 x 4 = _____	8 x 10 = _____
10 x 4 = _____	10 x 11 = _____	1 x 10 = _____
10 x 1 = _____	10 x 7 = _____	4 x 10 = _____
10 x 3 = _____	10 x 6 = _____	3 x 10 = _____

Keeping Track — Do the x10 Wrap-Ups for 3 minutes.

Keeping Track — Do the x10 Wrap-Ups for 3 minutes.

Time _____   **Time** _____   **Time** _____

★ **Shaded areas are problems you have already learned!** ★

★ **Meet your Goal**
Do the x10 Wrap-Up™ until you meet your goal.

1 minute	45 seconds	30 seconds	20 seconds	15 seconds	10 seconds
Getting started!	First goal. Keep going!	Champ!	Super Champ!	Awesome!	Next to impossible!

12

Read each problem. Follow the directions.

---

1. Ammon places his trading cards in three rows with 10 cards in each row. Draw a picture that shows how Ammon's cards look.

   Write a multiplication problem (equation) and answer (product) that shows how many cards Ammon has.

---

2. Michelle's seashell collection is in a flat box. She has 10 columns. She has four seashells in each column. Draw a picture to show all of Michelle's seashells.

   Write the multiplication problem (equation) and answer (product) that shows how many seashells Michelle has.

---

3. Terrance has 5 boxes of apples with 10 apples in each box. Draw a picture that shows how Terrance's boxes look.

   Write a multiplication problem (equation) and answer (product) that shows how many apples Terrance has.

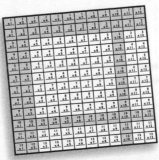

 You've mastered the 10s. You have **learned 63 facts**. Color in the chart on page 2.

Multiply. Shade in the bubble beside the correct product.

1

Sam's father has 10 boxes of nails. Each box has 12 nails. Which equation shows how many nails Sam's father has?

a) 10 x 10 = 100

b) 10 x 12 = 120

c) 12 x 10 = 111

d) None of these

2

Yolanda's sister has 2 boxes of crayons. Each box has 10 crayons. Which equation shows how many crayons Yolanda's sister has.

a) 2 x 10 = 20

b) 10 x 12 = 120

c) 10 x 2 = 22

d) None of these

3

Andy has 10 packets of stamps. Each packet has one stamp. Which equation shows how many stamps Andy has?

a) 2 x 5 = 10

b) 10 x 1 = 10

c) 10 x 2 = 20

d) None of these

4

Gloria's plant has 5 branches. Each branch has 10 leaves. Which equation shows how many leaves Gloria's plant has?

a) 2 x 5 = 10

b) 1 x 10 = 10

c) 10 x 7 = 70

d) None of these

Multiply by 3
Concept & Commutative

Think About It!

3×3

1 2 3

3 rows with 3 boxes
$3 \times 3 =$ _____

3×4

1 2 3

3 columns with 4 boxes
$3 \times 4 =$ _____

4 boxes in all 3 rows
$4 \times 3 =$ _____

3×6

1 2 3

3 columns with 6 boxes
$3 \times 6 =$ _____

6 boxes in all 3 columns
$6 \times 3 =$ _____

3×10

1
2
3

3 rows with 10 boxes
$3 \times 10 =$ _____

10 boxes in all 3 rows
$10 \times 3 =$ _____

rows: across

columns: up and down

Multiply.

3 ×1	1 ×3	3 ×2	2 ×3
3 ×3	3 ×3	3 ×4	4 ×3
3 ×5	5 ×3	3 ×6	6 ×3
3 ×7	7 ×3	3 ×8	8 ×3
3 ×9	9 ×3	3 ×10	10 ×3
3 ×11	11 ×3	3 ×12	12 ×3

Write all the 3 times tables and their commutative partners.

$3 \times 1 = 3$ _____ $1 \times 3 = 3$ _____

_____   _____

_____   _____

_____   _____

15

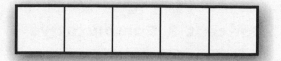

Do the x3 Wrap-Up™ 5 times. Mark an X in the box each time you finish.

1. Write the answers to the problems in the first column as fast as you can.
2. Do the x3 Learning Wrap-Up™ until you meet your goal. Mark a box in the Keeping Track section each time you complete the Wrap-Up™.
3. Write the answers to the second and third columns as fast as you can.

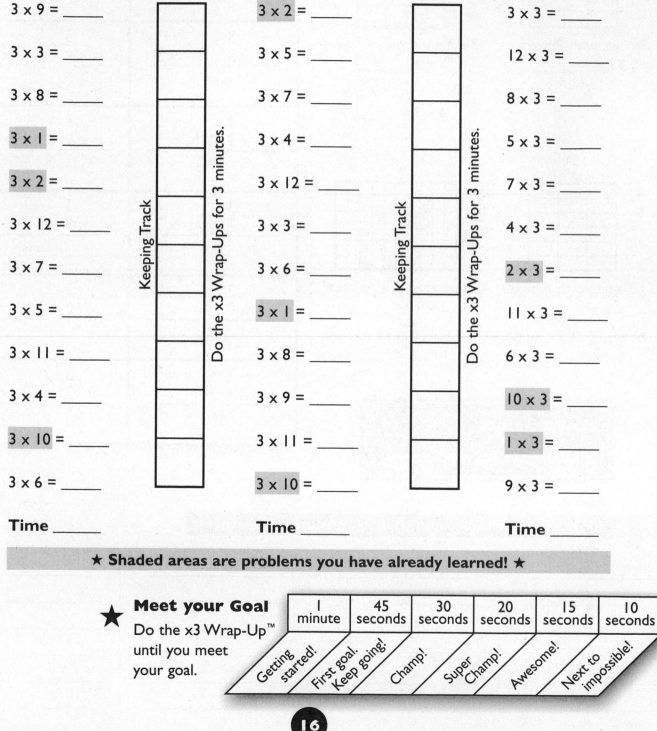

3 x 9 = _____

3 x 3 = _____

3 x 8 = _____

3 x 1 = _____

3 x 2 = _____

3 x 12 = _____

3 x 7 = _____

3 x 5 = _____

3 x 11 = _____

3 x 4 = _____

3 x 10 = _____

3 x 6 = _____

Keeping Track

Do the x3 Wrap-Ups for 3 minutes.

3 x 2 = _____

3 x 5 = _____

3 x 7 = _____

3 x 4 = _____

3 x 12 = _____

3 x 3 = _____

3 x 6 = _____

3 x 1 = _____

3 x 8 = _____

3 x 9 = _____

3 x 11 = _____

3 x 10 = _____

Keeping Track

Do the x3 Wrap-Ups for 3 minutes.

3 x 3 = _____

12 x 3 = _____

8 x 3 = _____

5 x 3 = _____

7 x 3 = _____

4 x 3 = _____

2 x 3 = _____

11 x 3 = _____

6 x 3 = _____

10 x 3 = _____

1 x 3 = _____

9 x 3 = _____

Time _____

Time _____

Time _____

★ **Shaded areas are problems you have already learned!** ★

★ **Meet your Goal**
Do the x3 Wrap-Up™ until you meet your goal.

1 minute	45 seconds	30 seconds	20 seconds	15 seconds	10 seconds
Getting started!	First goal. Keep going!	Champ!	Super Champ!	Awesome!	Next to impossible!

16

Day 2 — Story Problems

Read each problem. Follow the directions.

---

1. Caryn had 3 strings. She had 8 beads on each string. Draw a picture showing Caryn's strings and beads.

Write an equation and product to show how many beads Caryn had.

---

2. Natalie invented a game. It was for 3 players. Each player had 7 marbles. Draw the marbles for each player.

Write an equation and product that shows how many marbles are needed for everyone to play.

---

3. Mark invented a game, too. It was for 4 players. Each player had 3 marbles. Draw the marbles for Mark's game.

Write an equation and product that tells how many marbles are needed for Mark's game.

 You've mastered the 3s. You have **learned 80 facts**. Color in the chart on page 2.

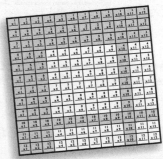

Write "the skip-counting by 3" numbers in the TRIANGLES, three times.

Shade all of the numbers that are not part of the x3 number family.

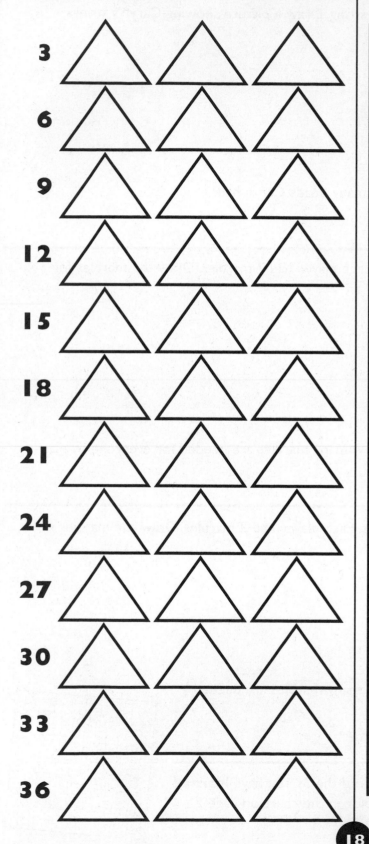

3
6
9
12
15
18
21
24
27
30
33
36

1	2	3	4	5
6	7	8	9	10
11	12	13	14	15
16	17	18	19	20
21	22	23	24	25
26	27	28	29	30
31	32	33	34	35
36	37	38	39	40

Day 2 — x3 Number Family Fun Page

Color each product and its two sets of factors the same color. Use a different color for each product.

Color all of the products in the x3 number family green.

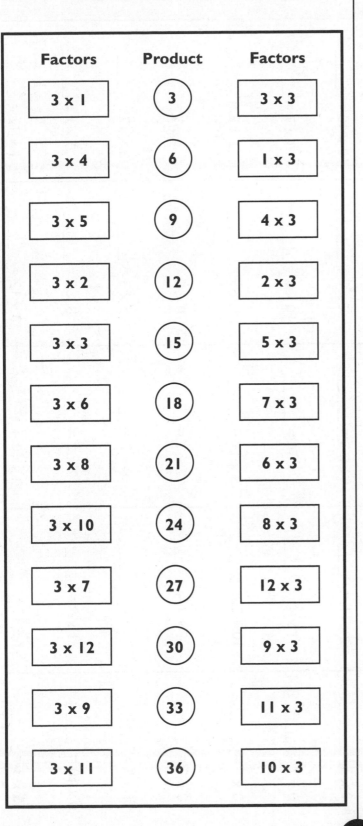

Factors	Product	Factors
3 x 1	3	3 x 3
3 x 4	6	1 x 3
3 x 5	9	4 x 3
3 x 2	12	2 x 3
3 x 3	15	5 x 3
3 x 6	18	7 x 3
3 x 8	21	6 x 3
3 x 10	24	8 x 3
3 x 7	27	12 x 3
3 x 12	30	9 x 3
3 x 9	33	11 x 3
3 x 11	36	10 x 3

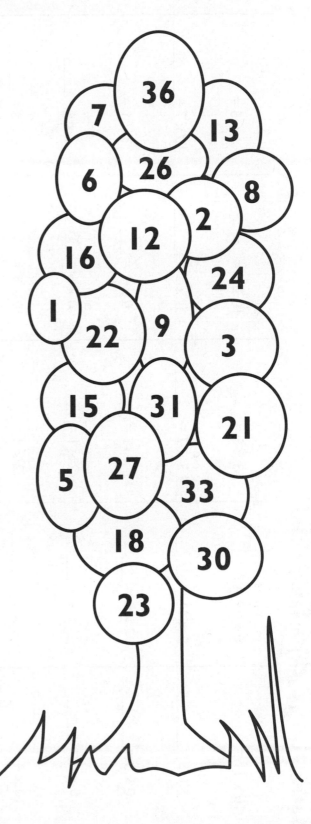

Challenge and Review

$3 \times 6 =$ _____	$1 \times 6 =$ _____	$10 \times 1 =$ _____	$3 \times 5 =$ _____	$0 \times 12 =$ _____
$10 \times 5 =$ _____	$10 \times 7 =$ _____	$1 \times 2 =$ _____	$3 \times 2 =$ _____	$2 \times 11 =$ _____
$3 \times 11 =$ _____	$3 \times 1 =$ _____	$10 \times 3 =$ _____	$2 \times 12 =$ _____	$2 \times 6 =$ _____
$2 \times 7 =$ _____	$3 \times 4 =$ _____	$0 \times 6 =$ _____	$2 \times 1 =$ _____	$1 \times 1 =$ _____
$1 \times 12 =$ _____	$0 \times 5 =$ _____	$10 \times 5 =$ _____	$2 \times 4 =$ _____	$1 \times 3 =$ _____
$0 \times 11 =$ _____	$10 \times 10 =$ _____	$2 \times 7 =$ _____	$1 \times 5 =$ _____	$0 \times 11 =$ _____
$10 \times 10 =$ _____	$3 \times 7 =$ _____	$10 \times 6 =$ _____	$1 \times 10 =$ _____	$1 \times 4 =$ _____
$2 \times 5 =$ _____	$2 \times 9 =$ _____	$0 \times 9 =$ _____	$3 \times 11 =$ _____	$10 \times 2 =$ _____
$3 \times 8 =$ _____	$3 \times 9 =$ _____	$10 \times 8 =$ _____	$2 \times 2 =$ _____	$1 \times 7 =$ _____
$10 \times 11 =$ _____	$3 \times 12 =$ _____	$2 \times 3 =$ _____	$0 \times 2 =$ _____	$3 \times 10 =$ _____
$3 \times 9 =$ _____	$0 \times 1 =$ _____	$3 \times 8 =$ _____	$2 \times 8 =$ _____	$1 \times 9 =$ _____
$3 \times 4 =$ _____	$1 \times 12 =$ _____	$10 \times 12 =$ _____	$2 \times 10 =$ _____	$1 \times 11 =$ _____

$10 \times 11 =$ _____
$3 \times 6 =$ _____
$0 \times 3 =$ _____
$0 \times 4 =$ _____
$10 \times 4 =$ _____
$2 \times 5 =$ _____
$0 \times 7 =$ _____
$10 \times 9 =$ _____
$0 \times 8 =$ _____
$1 \times 8 =$ _____
$0 \times 10 =$ _____
$3 \times 3 =$ _____

Multiply by 11
Concept & Commutative

Learning to multiply by 11 is a lot like multiplying by 1. Do you see a pattern?

11	11	11	11	11	11	11	11	11
x 1	x 2	x 3	x 4	x 5	x 6	x 7	x 8	x 9
11	22	33	44	55	66	77	88	99

Later in this lesson we will teach tricks for 11 x 11, and 11 x 12.

Concept:
Multiplying by 11 is like all other times tables.

```
   3  rows with  ★★★★★★★★★★★
x 11  stars      ★★★★★★★★★★★
 ----            ★★★★★★★★★★★
  33
```

```
  11  rows with  ★ ★ ★
x  3  stars      ★ ★ ★
 ----            ★ ★ ★
  33             ★ ★ ★
                 ★ ★ ★
                 ★ ★ ★
                 ★ ★ ★
                 ★ ★ ★
                 ★ ★ ★
                 ★ ★ ★
                 ★ ★ ★
```

Multiply.

11	1	11	2
x 1	x 11	x 2	x 11

11	3	11	4
x 3	x 11	x 4	x 11

11	5	11	6
x 5	x 11	x 6	x 11

11	7	11	8
x 7	x 11	x 8	x 11

11	9	11	10
x 9	x 11	x 10	x 11

Write all the 11 times tables and their commutative partners.

11 x 1 = 11   1 x 11 = 11

21

Day 3 Wrap-Ups and Rapid Writing

There is no Wrap-Up™ for x11. Use the drawing of an 11 Wrap-Up™ and draw lines from the questions on the right to the answers on the left.

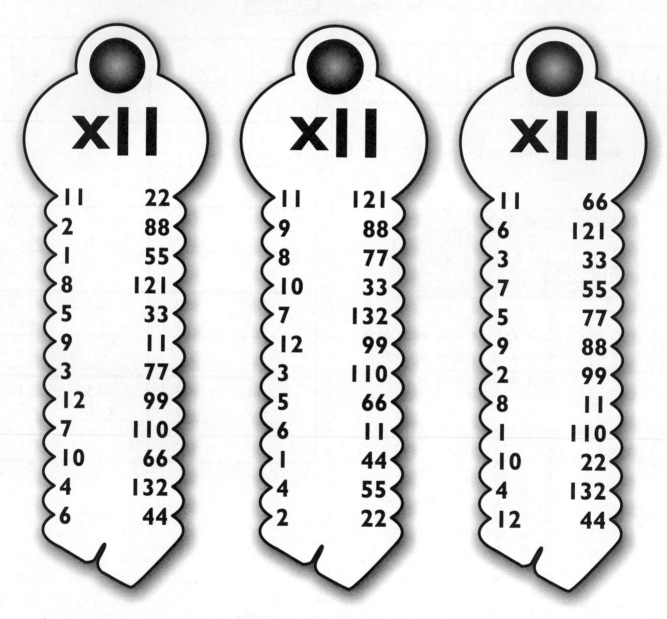

x11			x11			x11	
11	22		11	121		11	66
2	88		9	88		6	121
1	55		8	77		3	33
8	121		10	33		7	55
5	33		7	132		5	77
9	11		12	99		9	88
3	77		3	110		2	99
12	99		5	66		8	11
7	110		6	11		1	110
10	66		1	44		10	22
4	132		4	55		4	132
6	44		2	22		12	44

Write as fast as you can.

11 x 3	11 x 7	11 x 11	11 x 2	11 x 6	11 x 5	11 x 9	11 x 1	11 x 10	11 x 4	11 x 12	11 x 8
5 x 11	7 x 11	10 x 11	6 x 11	3 x 11	9 x 11	1 x 11	4 x 11	11 x 11	2 x 11	8 x 11	12 x 11

22

Day 3 Enrichment

Amaze your Friends

Multiplying bigger 2 digit numbers by 11 is fun. Try this trick.

1. Write a 2 digit number.
   Leave a space between the digits.

2. Add the 2 digits.

3. Write the sum in the space.

Example: 11 x 32

Write: 32 as 3 ___ 2.

Think: 3 + 2 = 5.

Solve: 11 x 32 = 352

Multiply.

Column 1

24 x 11 = ___ ___ ___

90 x 11 = ___ ___ ___

40 x 11 = ___ ___ ___

18 x 11 = ___ ___ ___

81 x 11 = ___ ___ ___

27 x 11 = ___ ___ ___

52 x 11 = ___ ___ ___

63 x 11 = ___ ___ ___

25 x 11 = ___ ___ ___

72 x 11 = ___ ___ ___

10 x 11 = ___ ___ ___

21 x 11 = ___ ___ ___

12 x 11 = ___ ___ ___

Column 2

35 x 11 = ___ ___ ___

61 x 11 = ___ ___ ___

14 x 11 = ___ ___ ___

54 x 11 = ___ ___ ___

33 x 11 = ___ ___ ___

16 x 11 = ___ ___ ___

13 x 11 = ___ ___ ___

41 x 11 = ___ ___ ___

15 x 11 = ___ ___ ___

45 x 11 = ___ ___ ___

33 x 11 = ___ ___ ___

20 x 11 = ___ ___ ___

36 x 11 = ___ ___ ___

Remember:

A digit is one of the numerals in a written number. In the number 25, the numerals 2 and 5 are digits.

 ★ WOW!

You've mastered the 11s.
You have **learned 95 facts.**
Color in the chart on page 2.

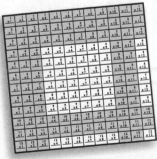

Amaze Your Friends

Some numbers need another step.

1. Write a 2 digit number. Leave a space between the digits.
2. Add the 2 digits.
3. If the sum is 10 or more, go to step 4.
4. Carry the 10s digit to the 100's column and add.
5. Write the 1s digit in the space.

Example: 11 x 39

Write: 39 as 3 ___ 9

Think: 3 + 9 = 12
Carry the 1 from the 12

Add: 3 + 1 = 4

Solve: 429

Multiply:

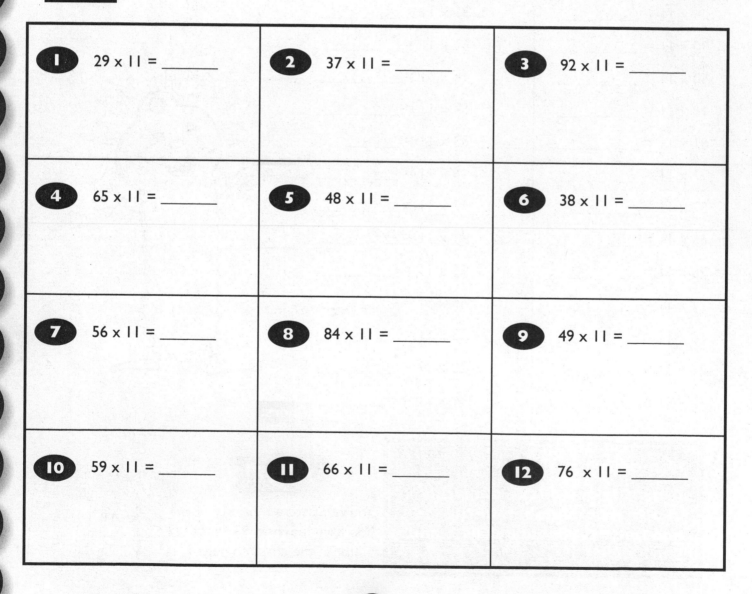

1 29 x 11 = _____	**2** 37 x 11 = _____	**3** 92 x 11 = _____
4 65 x 11 = _____	**5** 48 x 11 = _____	**6** 38 x 11 = _____
7 56 x 11 = _____	**8** 84 x 11 = _____	**9** 49 x 11 = _____
10 59 x 11 = _____	**11** 66 x 11 = _____	**12** 76 x 11 = _____

Multiply by 4

Concept & Commutative

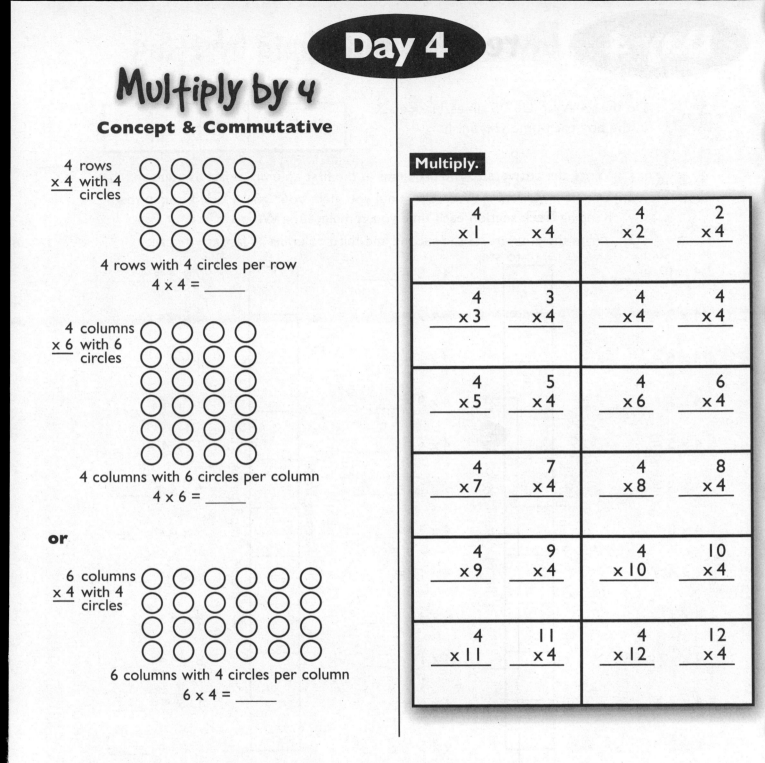

4 rows
x 4 with 4
circles

4 rows with 4 circles per row

4 x 4 = _____

4 columns
x 6 with 6
circles

4 columns with 6 circles per column

4 x 6 = _____

or

6 columns
x 4 with 4
circles

6 columns with 4 circles per column

6 x 4 = _____

Multiply.

4 x 1	1 x 4	4 x 2	2 x 4
4 x 3	3 x 4	4 x 4	4 x 4
4 x 5	5 x 4	4 x 6	6 x 4
4 x 7	7 x 4	4 x 8	8 x 4
4 x 9	9 x 4	4 x 10	10 x 4
4 x 11	11 x 4	4 x 12	12 x 4

Write all the 4 times tables and their commutative partners.

4 x 1 = 4 _____   1 x 4 = 4 _____

25

Do the x4 Wrap-Up™ 5 times. Mark an X in the box each time you finish.

1. Write the answers to the problems in the first column as fast as you can.
2. Do the x4 Learning Wrap-Up™ until you meet your goal. Mark a box in the Keeping Track section each time you complete the Wrap-Up™.
3. Write the answers to the second and third columns as fast as you can.

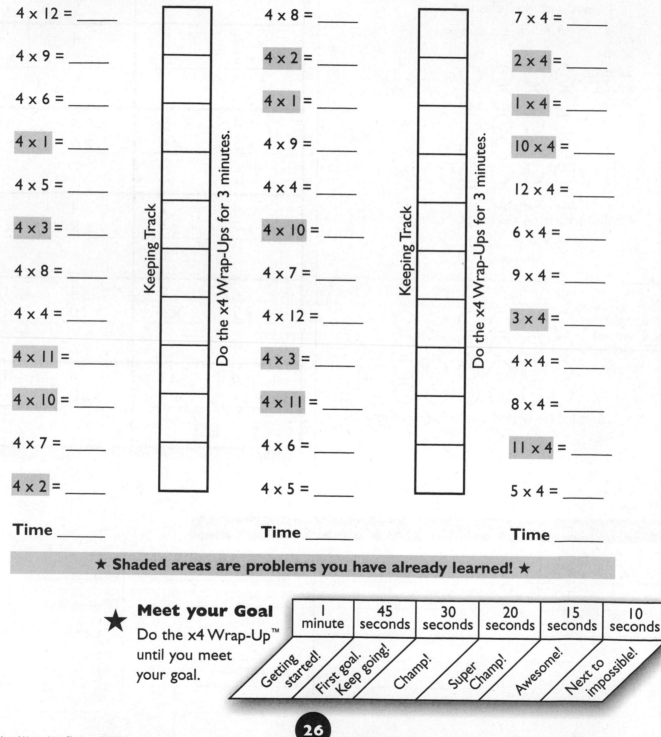

4 x 12 = _____

4 x 9 = _____

4 x 6 = _____

4 x 1 = _____

4 x 5 = _____

4 x 3 = _____

4 x 8 = _____

4 x 4 = _____

4 x 11 = _____

4 x 10 = _____

4 x 7 = _____

4 x 2 = _____

Time _____

Keeping Track

Do the x4 Wrap-Ups for 3 minutes.

4 x 8 = _____

4 x 2 = _____

4 x 1 = _____

4 x 9 = _____

4 x 4 = _____

4 x 10 = _____

4 x 7 = _____

4 x 12 = _____

4 x 3 = _____

4 x 11 = _____

4 x 6 = _____

4 x 5 = _____

Time _____

Keeping Track

Do the x4 Wrap-Ups for 3 minutes.

7 x 4 = _____

2 x 4 = _____

1 x 4 = _____

10 x 4 = _____

12 x 4 = _____

6 x 4 = _____

9 x 4 = _____

3 x 4 = _____

4 x 4 = _____

8 x 4 = _____

11 x 4 = _____

5 x 4 = _____

Time _____

★ **Shaded areas are problems you have already learned!** ★

★ **Meet your Goal**
Do the x4 Wrap-Up™ until you meet your goal.

1 minute	45 seconds	30 seconds	20 seconds	15 seconds	10 seconds
Getting started!	First goal. Keep going!	Champ!	Super Champ!	Awesome!	Next to impossible!

26

Day 4 Story Problems

Read each problem. Follow the directions.

1. Andra has 4 boxes. Each box has 6 peanuts in it. Draw a picture showing the peanuts in Andra's boxes.

   Write an equation and product to show how many peanuts there are.

2. Jeff collects rocks. He keeps them all in 6 glass jars. There are 4 rocks in each jar. Draw a picture showing Jeff's rocks and jars.

   Write an equation and product to show how many rocks he has in all.

3. Mollie keeps her hair barrettes in plastic bags. She has 4 bags and each one holds 9 barrettes. Draw a picture showing her bags and barrettes.

   Write an equation and product to show how many barrettes Mollie has in all.

 You've mastered the 4s. You have **learned 102 facts**. Color in the chart on page 2.

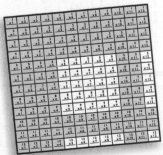

Skip count by 4 along the SQUARES path.

Circle the numbers that belong to the x4 family.

The 4, 20, and 48 crayons are numbered correctly. Can you write the x4 family numbers in order from largest to smallest in the ovals?

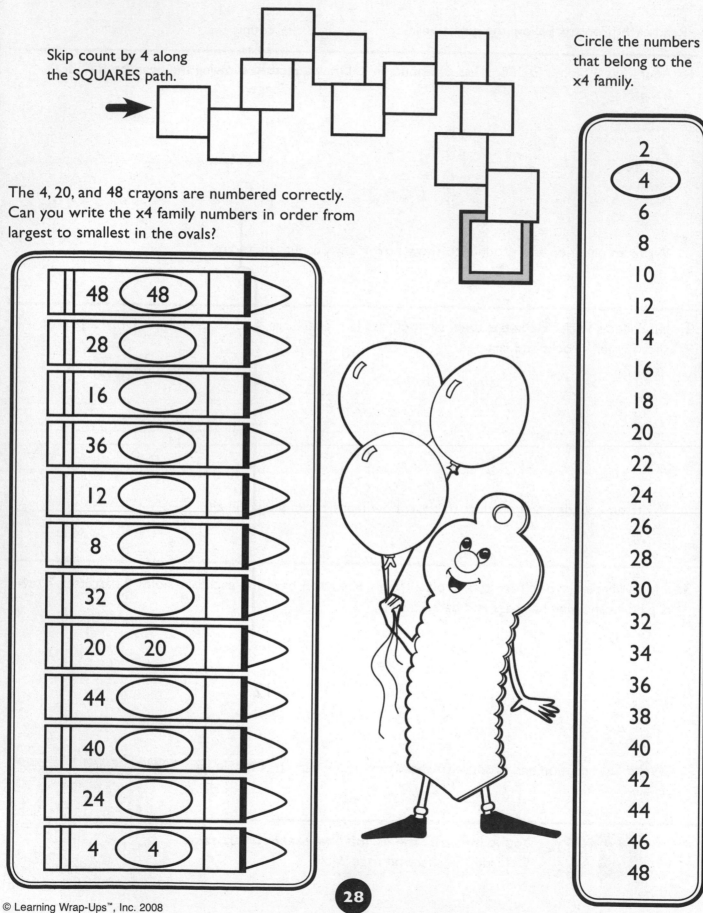

Crayon	Oval
48	48
28	
16	
36	
12	
8	
32	
20	20
44	
40	
24	
4	4

2
4
6
8
10
12
14
16
18
20
22
24
26
28
30
32
34
36
38
40
42
44
46
48

28

Day 4 x4 Number Family Fun Page

Start with the 4 and draw lines to the x4 products in order.

Skip count through the number maze. Circle each number as you come to it. Try to do it without lifting your pencil from the page.

Start

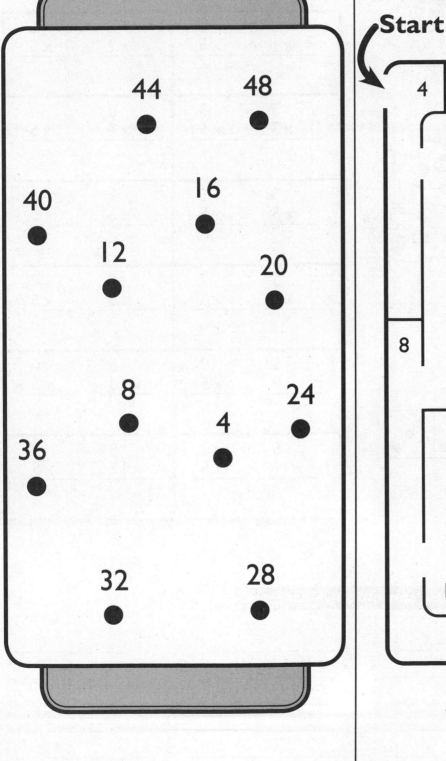

44   48

40

16

12

20

8   4   24

36

32   28

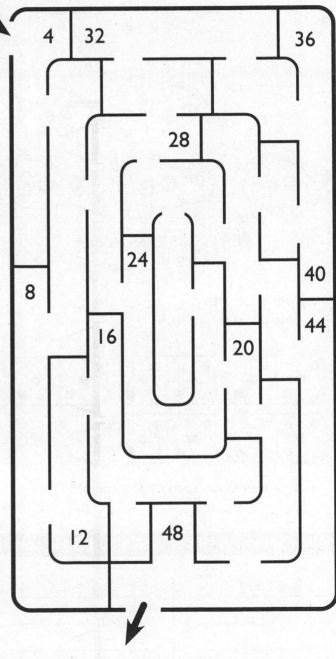

4   32   36

28

24   40

8   44

16   20

12   48

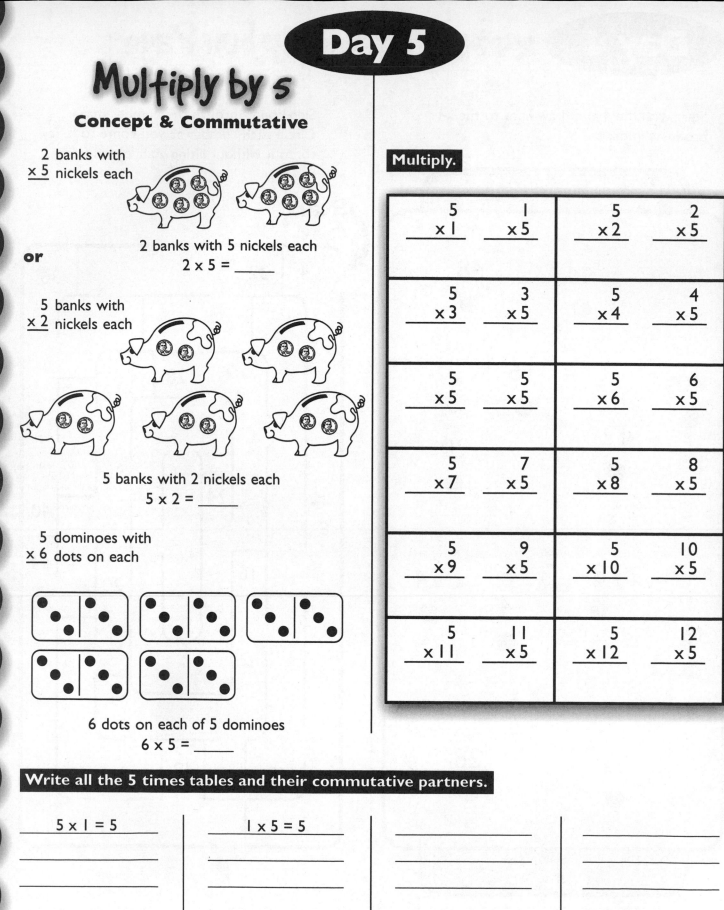

Multiply by 5
Concept & Commutative

2 banks with
x 5 nickels each

2 banks with 5 nickels each
2 x 5 = _____

or

5 banks with
x 2 nickels each

5 banks with 2 nickels each
5 x 2 = _____

5 dominoes with
x 6 dots on each

6 dots on each of 5 dominoes
6 x 5 = _____

Multiply.

5 x 1	1 x 5	5 x 2	2 x 5
5 x 3	3 x 5	5 x 4	4 x 5
5 x 5	5 x 5	5 x 6	6 x 5
5 x 7	7 x 5	5 x 8	8 x 5
5 x 9	9 x 5	5 x 10	10 x 5
5 x 11	11 x 5	5 x 12	12 x 5

Write all the 5 times tables and their commutative partners.

5 x 1 = 5   1 x 5 = 5

Do the x5 Wrap-Up™ 5 times. Mark an X in the box each time you finish.

1. Write the answers to the problems in the first column as fast as you can.
2. Do the x5 Learning Wrap-Up™ until you meet your goal. Mark a box in the Keeping Track section each time you complete the Wrap-Up™.
3. Write the answers to the second and third columns as fast as you can.

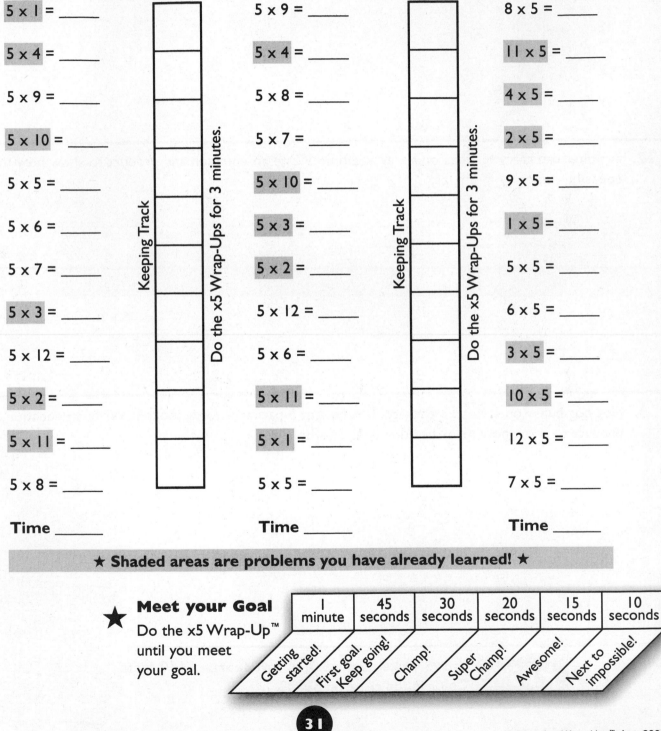

5 x 1 = _____

5 x 4 = _____

5 x 9 = _____

5 x 10 = _____

5 x 5 = _____

5 x 6 = _____

5 x 7 = _____

5 x 3 = _____

5 x 12 = _____

5 x 2 = _____

5 x 11 = _____

5 x 8 = _____

Time _____

Keeping Track

Do the x5 Wrap-Ups for 3 minutes.

5 x 9 = _____

5 x 4 = _____

5 x 8 = _____

5 x 7 = _____

5 x 10 = _____

5 x 3 = _____

5 x 2 = _____

5 x 12 = _____

5 x 6 = _____

5 x 11 = _____

5 x 1 = _____

5 x 5 = _____

Time _____

Keeping Track

Do the x5 Wrap-Ups for 3 minutes.

8 x 5 = _____

11 x 5 = _____

4 x 5 = _____

2 x 5 = _____

9 x 5 = _____

1 x 5 = _____

5 x 5 = _____

6 x 5 = _____

3 x 5 = _____

10 x 5 = _____

12 x 5 = _____

7 x 5 = _____

Time _____

★ Shaded areas are problems you have already learned! ★

★ **Meet your Goal**
Do the x5 Wrap-Up™ until you meet your goal.

1 minute	45 seconds	30 seconds	20 seconds	15 seconds	10 seconds
Getting started!	First goal. Keep going!	Champ!	Super Champ!	Awesome!	Next to impossible!

31

Solve these problems and write the equation including the product. You do not have to draw pictures unless you want to.

1. Josh made up a game called Pentagon Ball. It takes 5 players to play the game. There is room in the gym to play 8 games at the same time. Write an equation and product to show how many children can play Pentagon Ball at the same time.

2. A waiter can carry 8 sodas on a tray at a time. Write an equation and product to show how many sodas he can carry in 5 trips.

3. Hot dog buns come 12 to a package. Tina bought 5 packages for a cookout. Write an equation and product to show how many hot dog buns Tina bought.

 You've mastered the 5s. You have **learned 119 facts**. Color in the chart on page 2.

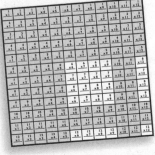

32

The number family for 5 is also called the product of the factors five multiplied by _____. Fill in the factor that has not been written.

Start with 5 and draw lines to the x5 products in order. Use only members of the x5 number family.

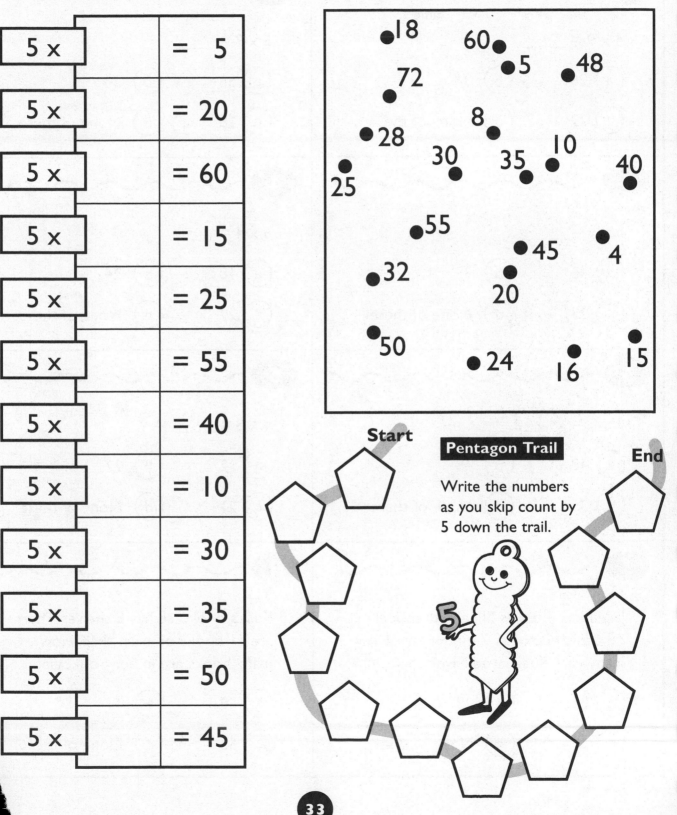

5 x	= 5
5 x	= 20
5 x	= 60
5 x	= 15
5 x	= 25
5 x	= 55
5 x	= 40
5 x	= 10
5 x	= 30
5 x	= 35
5 x	= 50
5 x	= 45

18
60
72 • 5 • 48
8
28
30 35 10
25
40
55
32 45 4
20
50
24 16 15

Start

Pentagon Trail

End

Write the numbers as you skip count by 5 down the trail.

Multiply. Shade in the correct bubble.

1

$4 \times 9 = \underline{\hspace{1cm}}$

(a) 28   (b) 36

(c) 32   (d) None of these

2

$5 \times 7 = \underline{\hspace{1cm}}$

(a) 35   (b) 30

(c) 28   (d) None of these

3

$5 \times 5 = \underline{\hspace{1cm}}$

(a) 45   (b) 35

(c) 25   (d) None of these

4

$6 \times 4 = \underline{\hspace{1cm}}$

(a) 18   (b) 24

(c) 22   (d) None of these

5

$8 \times 5 = \underline{\hspace{1cm}}$

(a) 40   (b) 48

(c) 35   (d) None of these

6

$4 \times 8 = \underline{\hspace{1cm}}$

(a) 32   (b) 27

(c) 21   (d) None of these

7

Jared has 4 boxes filled with model cars. Each box has 7 model cars. How many cars does Jared have?

(a) 24   (b) 28

(c) 20   (d) None of these

8

Kaila's bookcase has 5 shelves. There are 11 books on each shelf. How many books are in her bookcase?

(a) 50   (b) 11

(c) 55   (d) None of these

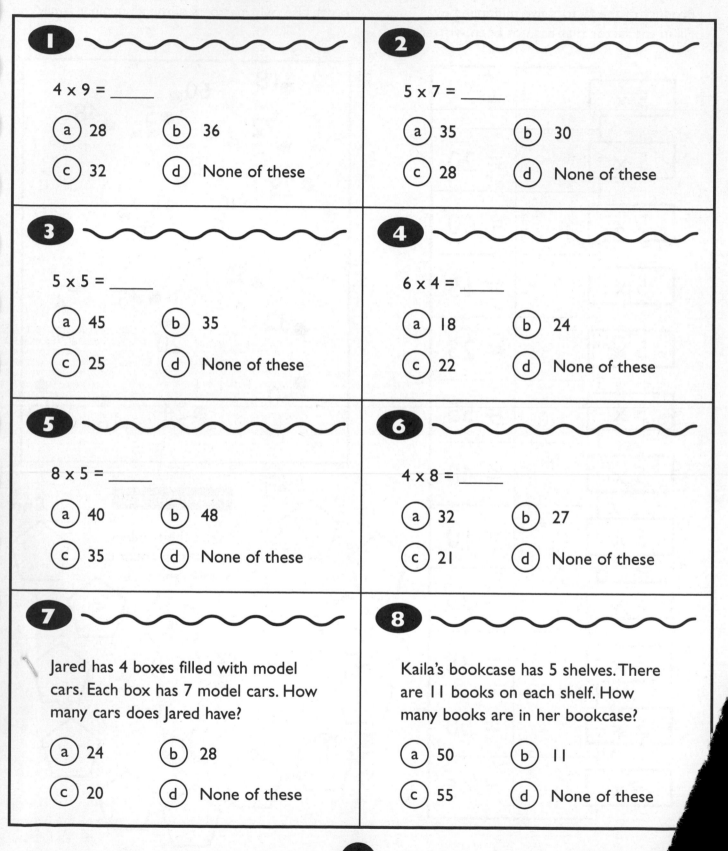

Day 5 — Perfect Squares

Think About It!

Square equations do not have commutative partners. They have the same two factors. You have already learned 1 x 1, 2 x 2, 10 x 10, 3 x 3, 11 x 11, 4 x 4, and 5 x 5.

You only have 5 perfect squares left to learn. They are 6 x 6 = 36, 7 x 7 = 49, 8 x 8 = 64, 9 x 9 = 81, and 12 x 12 = 144.

Write the product for each of the grids.

2 x 2 = _____

1 x 1 = _____

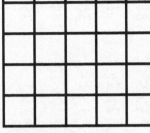

5 x 5 = _____

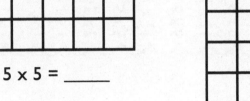

8 x 8 = _____

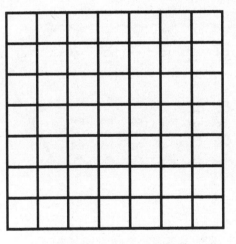

7 x 7 = _____

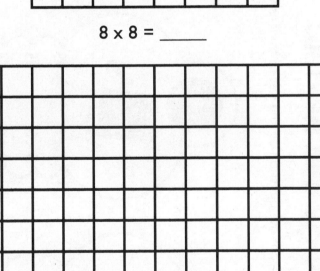

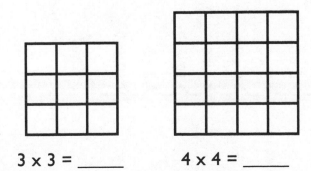

3 x 3 = _____

4 x 4 = _____

35

12 x 12 = _____

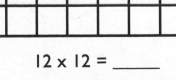

Draw lines from the question on the left to the answer on the right.

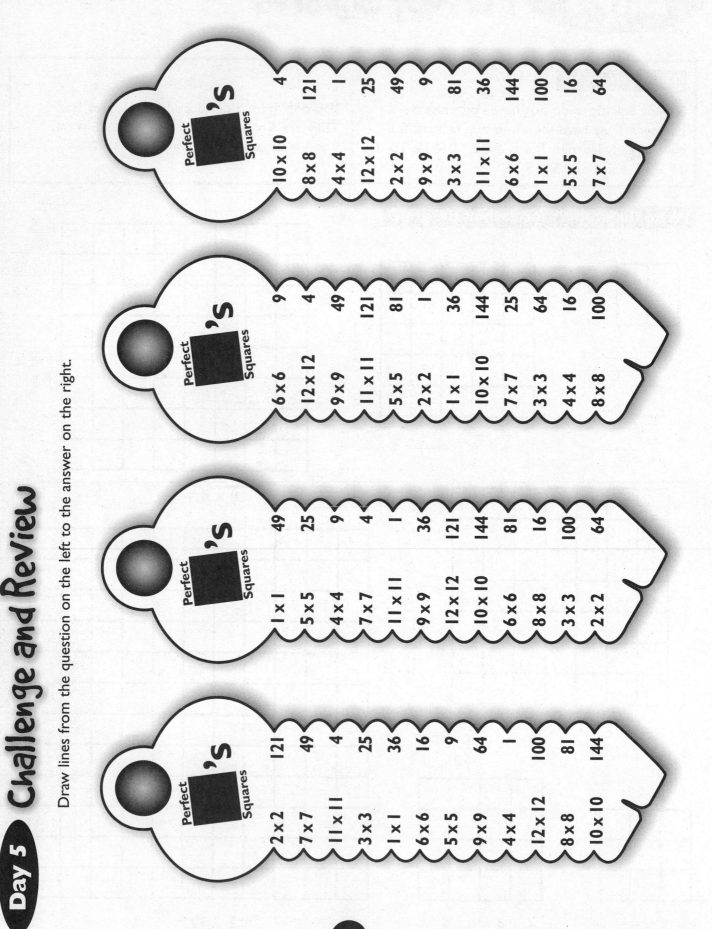

Perfect 's Squares

10 x 10	4
8 x 8	121
4 x 4	1
12 x 12	25
2 x 2	49
9 x 9	9
3 x 3	81
11 x 11	36
6 x 6	144
1 x 1	100
5 x 5	16
7 x 7	64

Perfect 's Squares

6 x 6	9
12 x 12	4
9 x 9	49
11 x 11	121
5 x 5	81
2 x 2	1
1 x 1	36
10 x 10	144
7 x 7	25
3 x 3	64
4 x 4	16
8 x 8	100

Perfect 's Squares

1 x 1	49
5 x 5	25
4 x 4	9
7 x 7	4
11 x 11	1
9 x 9	36
12 x 12	121
10 x 10	144
6 x 6	81
8 x 8	16
3 x 3	100
2 x 2	64

Perfect 's Squares

2 x 2	121
7 x 7	49
11 x 11	4
3 x 3	25
1 x 1	36
6 x 6	16
5 x 5	9
9 x 9	64
4 x 4	1
12 x 12	100
8 x 8	81
10 x 10	144

Multiply by 6
Concept & Commutative

7
x 6

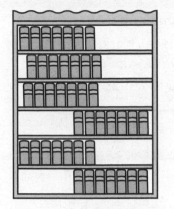

7 books on 6 shelves

$7 \times 6 =$ _____

or

6
x 7

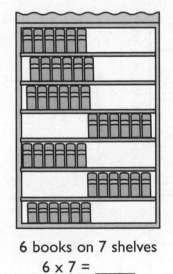

6 books on 7 shelves

$6 \times 7 =$ _____

Multiply.

6 x 1	1 x 6	6 x 2	2 x 6
6 x 3	3 x 6	6 x 4	4 x 6
6 x 5	5 x 6	6 x 6	6 x 6
6 x 7	7 x 6	6 x 8	8 x 6
6 x 9	9 x 6	6 x 10	10 x 6
6 x 11	11 x 6	6 x 12	12 x 6

Write all the 6 times tables and their commutative partners.

$6 \times 1 = 6$ $1 \times 6 = 6$

_____

_____

_____

_____

_____

37

Day 6

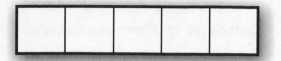

Do the x6 Wrap-Up™ 5 times. Mark an X in the box each time you finish.

1. Write the answers to the problems in the first column as fast as you can.
2. Do the x6 Learning Wrap-Up™ until you meet your goal. Mark a box in the Keeping Track section each time you complete the Wrap-Up™.
3. Write the answers to the second and third columns as fast as you can.

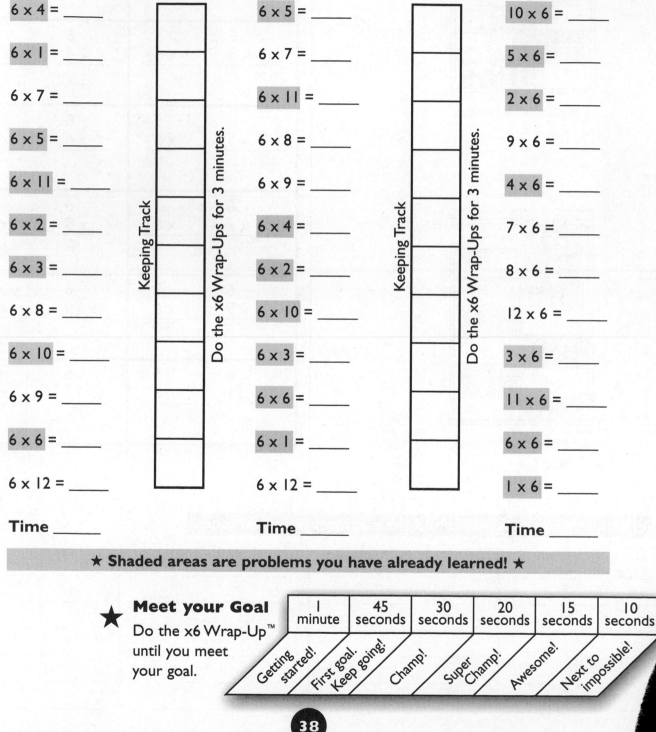

6 x 4 = _____   6 x 5 = _____   10 x 6 = _____

6 x 1 = _____   6 x 7 = _____   5 x 6 = _____

6 x 7 = _____   6 x 11 = _____   2 x 6 = _____

6 x 5 = _____   6 x 8 = _____   9 x 6 = _____

6 x 11 = _____   6 x 9 = _____   4 x 6 = _____

6 x 2 = _____   6 x 4 = _____   7 x 6 = _____

6 x 3 = _____   6 x 2 = _____   8 x 6 = _____

6 x 8 = _____   6 x 10 = _____   12 x 6 = _____

6 x 10 = _____   6 x 3 = _____   3 x 6 = _____

6 x 9 = _____   6 x 6 = _____   11 x 6 = _____

6 x 6 = _____   6 x 1 = _____   6 x 6 = _____

6 x 12 = _____   6 x 12 = _____   1 x 6 = _____

Keeping Track / Do the x6 Wrap-Ups for 3 minutes.

Keeping Track / Do the x6 Wrap-Ups for 3 minutes.

Time _____   **Time** _____   **Time** _____

★ Shaded areas are problems you have already learned! ★

★ **Meet your Goal**
Do the x6 Wrap-Up™ until you meet your goal.

1 minute	45 seconds	30 seconds	20 seconds	15 seconds	10 seconds
Getting started!	First goal. Keep going!	Champ!	Super Champ!	Awesome!	Next to impossible!

38

Day 6 Story Problems

Solve each problem. Shade in the correct bubble.

1. Jake drew a creature with 6 arms. Each arm had 2 hands. How many hands in all?

   a) 16   b) 24

   c) 6   d) 12

   e) none of these

2. Kira drew a creature with 6 tails. Each tail had 5 purple spots. How many spots in all?

   a) 24   b) 30

   c) 20   d) 36

   e) none of these

3. Spencer drew a creature with 6 mouths. Each mouth had 9 teeth. How many teeth in all?

   a) 50   b) 36

   c) 60   d) 54

   e) none of these

4. Maria's creature had 7 eyebrows over each eye. It had 6 eyes. How many eyebrows?

   a) 42   b) 40

   c) 36   d) 49

   e) none of these

★WOW! You've mastered perfect squares and the 6s. You have **learned 132 facts**. You have **only 12 left to learn** (actually 6 facts and their commutative partners)! Color in the chart on page 2.

39

Day 6 x6 Number Family Fun Page

Fill in the missing factors.

Skip count through the x6 number family four times. Each time you get to 72 start over with 6. Draw a path with your pencil.

This Silly Six Snake is about to shed its skin. It can keep only that skin which is numbered a multiple of 6. Help it by coloring the spots that are not multiples of 6.

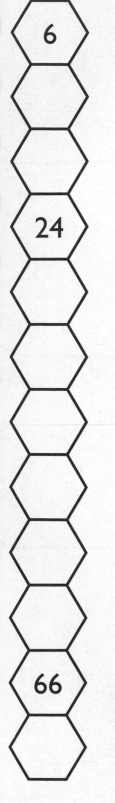

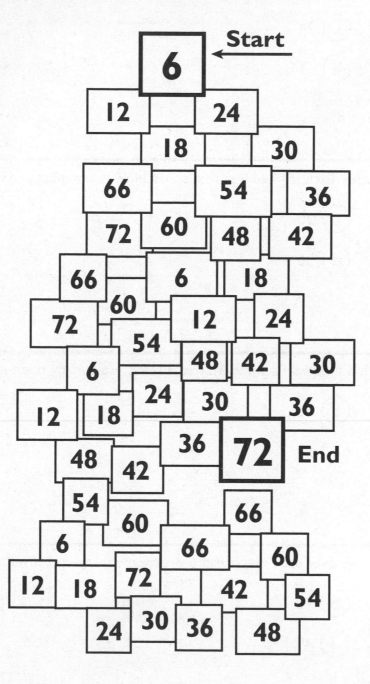

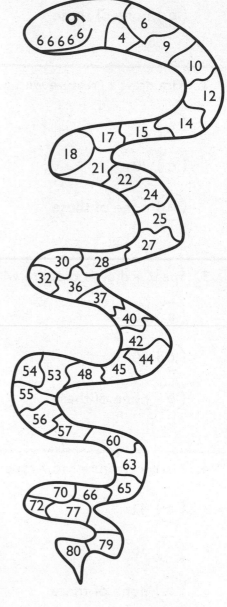

40

© Learning Wrap-Ups™, Inc. 2008

Multiply by 9
Concept & Commutative

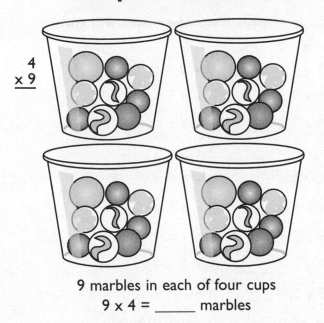

$$\begin{array}{r} 4 \\ \times\,9 \\ \hline \end{array}$$

9 marbles in each of four cups

$9 \times 4 = \underline{\qquad}$ marbles

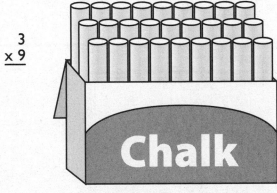

$$\begin{array}{r} 3 \\ \times\,9 \\ \hline \end{array}$$

Chalk

9 sticks of chalk in each of 3 rows

$9 \times 3 = \underline{\qquad}$

Multiply.

$\begin{array}{r}9\\ \times 1\\ \hline\end{array}$	$\begin{array}{r}1\\ \times 9\\ \hline\end{array}$	$\begin{array}{r}9\\ \times 2\\ \hline\end{array}$	$\begin{array}{r}2\\ \times 9\\ \hline\end{array}$
$\begin{array}{r}9\\ \times 3\\ \hline\end{array}$	$\begin{array}{r}3\\ \times 9\\ \hline\end{array}$	$\begin{array}{r}9\\ \times 4\\ \hline\end{array}$	$\begin{array}{r}4\\ \times 9\\ \hline\end{array}$
$\begin{array}{r}9\\ \times 5\\ \hline\end{array}$	$\begin{array}{r}5\\ \times 9\\ \hline\end{array}$	$\begin{array}{r}9\\ \times 6\\ \hline\end{array}$	$\begin{array}{r}6\\ \times 9\\ \hline\end{array}$
$\begin{array}{r}9\\ \times 7\\ \hline\end{array}$	$\begin{array}{r}7\\ \times 9\\ \hline\end{array}$	$\begin{array}{r}9\\ \times 8\\ \hline\end{array}$	$\begin{array}{r}8\\ \times 9\\ \hline\end{array}$
$\begin{array}{r}9\\ \times 9\\ \hline\end{array}$	$\begin{array}{r}9\\ \times 9\\ \hline\end{array}$	$\begin{array}{r}9\\ \times 10\\ \hline\end{array}$	$\begin{array}{r}10\\ \times 9\\ \hline\end{array}$
$\begin{array}{r}9\\ \times 11\\ \hline\end{array}$	$\begin{array}{r}11\\ \times 9\\ \hline\end{array}$	$\begin{array}{r}9\\ \times 12\\ \hline\end{array}$	$\begin{array}{r}12\\ \times 9\\ \hline\end{array}$

Write all the 9 times tables and their commutative partners.

$9 \times 1 = 9$ _____ $1 \times 9 = 9$ _____   _____   _____

_____   _____   _____   _____

_____   _____   _____   _____

_____   _____   _____   _____

_____   _____   _____   _____

41

9s Are Easy!

Here is a fun strategy!

Think one less than the number you are multiplying by.

Next, think of a number that can be added to it which will total 9.

Those two numbers are the answer.

Example: 9 x 4

Think: I less than 4 is 3.
$3 + 6 = 9$.
So, the answer is **36**

Example: 9 x 8

Think: I less than 8 is 7.
$7 + 2 = 9$.
So, the answer is **72**

Think:

I less than __ is __ plus a number that will total 9.

$9 \times 1 =$ _____ $0 + 9 = 9$
$9 \times 2 =$ _____ $1 + 8 = 9$
$9 \times 3 =$ _____ $2 + 7 = 9$
$9 \times 4 =$ _____ $3 + 6 = 9$
$9 \times 5 =$ _____ $4 + 5 = 9$
$9 \times 6 =$ _____ $5 + 4 = 9$
$9 \times 7 =$ _____ $6 + 3 = 9$
$9 \times 8 =$ _____ $7 + 2 = 9$
$9 \times 9 =$ _____ $8 + 1 = 9$
$9 \times 10 =$ _____   use the 10 rule
$9 \times 11 =$ _____   use the 11 rule
$9 \times 12 =$ _____   108 (memorize)

$9 \times 1 =$ _____	$10 \times 9 =$ _____	$12 \times 9 =$ _____
$9 \times 2 =$ _____	$3 \times 9 =$ _____	$2 \times 9 =$ _____
$9 \times 3 =$ _____	$9 \times 9 =$ _____	$4 \times 9 =$ _____
$9 \times 4 =$ _____	$6 \times 9 =$ _____	$8 \times 9 =$ _____
$9 \times 5 =$ _____	$1 \times 9 =$ _____	$6 \times 9 =$ _____
$9 \times 6 =$ _____	$7 \times 9 =$ _____	$1 \times 9 =$ _____
$9 \times 7 =$ _____	$11 \times 9 =$ _____	$10 \times 9 =$ _____
$9 \times 8 =$ _____	$5 \times 9 =$ _____	$3 \times 9 =$ _____
$9 \times 9 =$ _____	$2 \times 9 =$ _____	$9 \times 9 =$ _____
$9 \times 10 =$ _____	$4 \times 9 =$ _____	$7 \times 9 =$ _____
$9 \times 11 =$ _____	$8 \times 9 =$ _____	$11 \times 9 =$ _____
$9 \times 12 =$ _____	$12 \times 9 =$ _____	$5 \times 9 =$ _____

Do the x9 Wrap-Up™ 5 times. Mark an X in the box each time you finish.

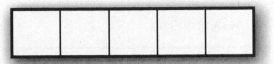

1. Write the answers to the problems in the first column as fast as you can.
2. Do the x9 Learning Wrap-Up™ until you meet your goal. Mark a box in the Keeping Track section each time you complete the Wrap-Up™.
3. Write the answers to the second and third columns as fast as you can.

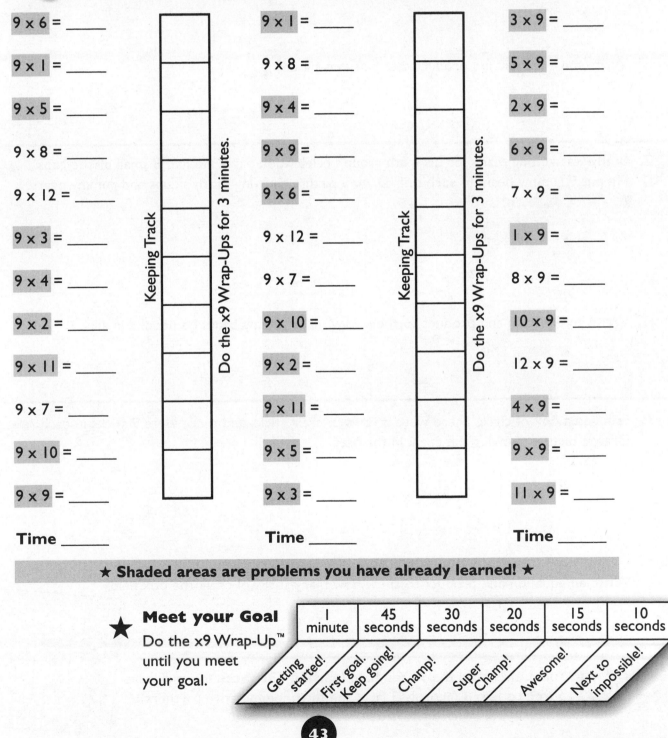

9 x 6 = ____		9 x 1 = ____		3 x 9 = ____
9 x 1 = ____		9 x 8 = ____		5 x 9 = ____
9 x 5 = ____		9 x 4 = ____		2 x 9 = ____
9 x 8 = ____		9 x 9 = ____		6 x 9 = ____
9 x 12 = ____		9 x 6 = ____		7 x 9 = ____
9 x 3 = ____	Keeping Track / Do the x9 Wrap-Ups for 3 minutes.	9 x 12 = ____		1 x 9 = ____
9 x 4 = ____		9 x 7 = ____	Keeping Track / Do the x9 Wrap-Ups for 3 minutes.	8 x 9 = ____
9 x 2 = ____		9 x 10 = ____		10 x 9 = ____
9 x 11 = ____		9 x 2 = ____		12 x 9 = ____
9 x 7 = ____		9 x 11 = ____		4 x 9 = ____
9 x 10 = ____		9 x 5 = ____		9 x 9 = ____
9 x 9 = ____		9 x 3 = ____		11 x 9 = ____

Time ____   **Time ____**   **Time ____**

★ Shaded areas are problems you have already learned! ★

★ **Meet your Goal**
Do the x9 Wrap-Up™ until you meet your goal.

1 minute	45 seconds	30 seconds	20 seconds	15 seconds	10 seconds
Getting started!	First goal. Keep going!	Champ!	Super Champ!	Awesome!	Next to impossible!

Solve these problems.

1. Jade wanted to model a multiplication equation. She made 9 bundles of toothpicks. Each bundle contained 8 toothpicks. Draw a picture showing Jade's bundles of toothpicks.

   Write the equation and product that Jade was modeling.

2. Brady was getting ready for his math group's celebration party. He had 8 small plastic cups. He put 9 gummy bears in each one. Draw a picture showing Brady's cups and gummy bears.

   Write an equation and product to show how many gummy bears he needed in all.

3. Erin had a box of chalk. There were 3 rows of chalk sticks and there were 9 sticks in each row. Draw a picture showing the chalk in the box.

   Write an equation and product to show how many sticks of chalk the box held.

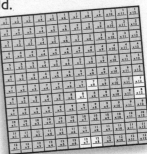

 You've mastered the 9s. You have **learned 138 facts.** You only have **6 left to learn** (actually 3 facts and their commutative partners)! Color in the chart on page 2.

Write the x9 family numbers two times.

9
18
27
36
45
54
63
72
81
90
99
108

Can you find your way to the center of this maze? You must pass through the x9 family numbers in order. Do not travel any path more than once. Try to do it without lifting your pencil off the paper.

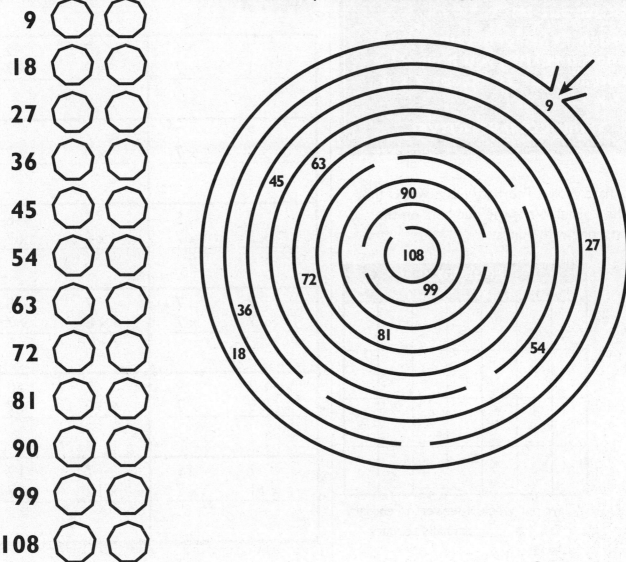

Draw a circle around the four numbers in each NONAGON that are not members of the x9 family.

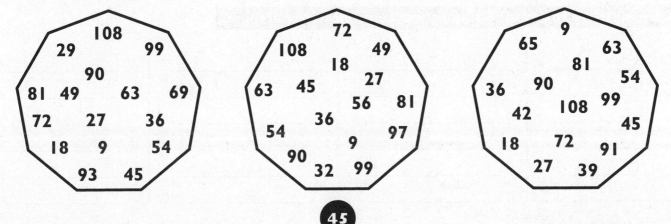

Multiply by 7
Concept & Commutative

Think About It!

Although 7s are generally considered HARD, you have learned all your 7s except 7 x 8 and 7 x 12.

Think COMMUTATIVE!

All weeks have 7 days. February has 4 weeks (not counting leap year). Write the numbers on the calendar starting with Sunday.

4 weeks
x 7 days per
    week

February						
Sun	**Mon**	**Tue**	**Wed**	**Thu**	**Fri**	**Sat**

7 days per week; 4 weeks in February

7 x 4 = _____ days in February

Multiply.

7 x 1	1 x 7	7 x 2	2 x 7
7 x 3	3 x 7	7 x 4	4 x 7
7 x 5	5 x 7	7 x 6	6 x 7
7 x 7	7 x 7	7 x 8	8 x 7
7 x 9	9 x 7	7 x 10	10 x 7
7 x 11	11 x 7	7 x 12	12 x 7

Write all the 7 times tables and their commutative partners.

7 x 1 = 7 _____   1 x 7 = 7 _____   _____   _____

_____   _____   _____   _____

_____   _____   _____   _____

_____   _____   _____   _____

_____   _____   _____   _____

Day 7

46

Do the x7 Wrap-Up™ 5 times. Mark an X in the box each time you finish.

1. Write the answers to the problems in the first column as fast as you can.
2. Do the x7 Learning Wrap-Up™ until you meet your goal. Mark a box in the Keeping Track section each time you complete the Wrap-Up™.
3. Write the answers to the second and third columns as fast as you can.

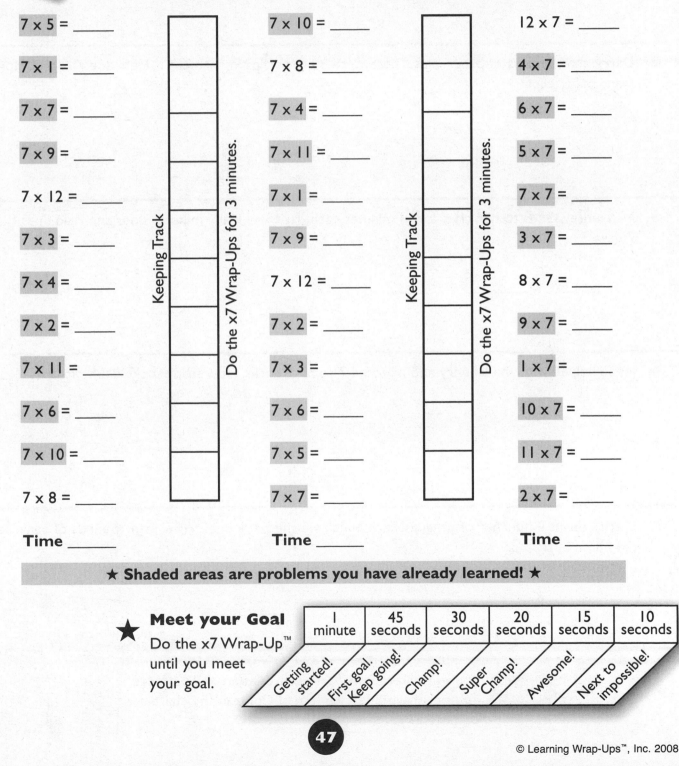

7 x 5 = _____	7 x 10 = _____	12 x 7 = _____
7 x 1 = _____	7 x 8 = _____	4 x 7 = _____
7 x 7 = _____	7 x 4 = _____	6 x 7 = _____
7 x 9 = _____	7 x 11 = _____	5 x 7 = _____
7 x 12 = _____	7 x 1 = _____	7 x 7 = _____
7 x 3 = _____	7 x 9 = _____	3 x 7 = _____
7 x 4 = _____	7 x 12 = _____	8 x 7 = _____
7 x 2 = _____	7 x 2 = _____	9 x 7 = _____
7 x 11 = _____	7 x 3 = _____	1 x 7 = _____
7 x 6 = _____	7 x 6 = _____	10 x 7 = _____
7 x 10 = _____	7 x 5 = _____	11 x 7 = _____
7 x 8 = _____	7 x 7 = _____	2 x 7 = _____

Keeping Track — Do the x7 Wrap-Ups for 3 minutes.

Time _____   **Time** _____   **Time** _____

★ **Shaded areas are problems you have already learned!** ★

★ **Meet your Goal**
Do the x7 Wrap-Up™ until you meet your goal.

1 minute	45 seconds	30 seconds	20 seconds	15 seconds	10 seconds
Getting started!	First goal. Keep going!	Champ!	Super Champ!	Awesome!	Next to impossible!

47

Write an equation and a product to solve each problem.

1. There are 7 days in a week. How many days in 6 weeks?

   _____ x _____ = _____

2. Darryl made chains of paper clips. There were 8 paper clips in each chain. He made 7 chains. How many paper clips?

   _____ x _____ = _____

3. Ms Lindsey reads to her class for 11 minutes each day. How many minutes does she read in 7 days?

   _____ x _____ = _____

4. Jessie helped with the laundry and matched 7 pairs of socks. How many socks did he match?

   _____ x _____ = _____

5. Mitch bought 7 bunches of bananas. Each bunch weighed 3 pounds. How many pounds of bananas did Mitch buy?

   _____ x _____ = _____

 You've mastered the 9s. You have **learned 142 facts**. You only have **2 left to learn!** Color in the chart on page 2.

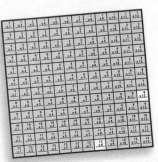

Day 7 x7 Number Family Fun Page

Multiply each of the numbers in the inner web by 7 and record your answers in the outer web.

Circle the three numbers in each HEPTAGON that do not belong to the x7 family.

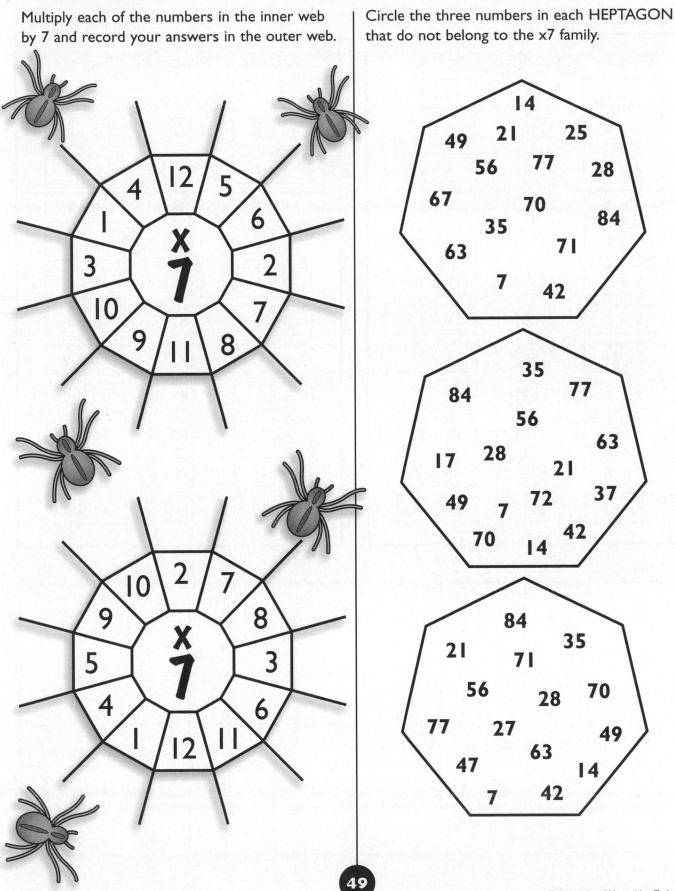

Draw lines from the factors to the correct product.

Factors	Product	Factors
7 x 1	7	3 x 7
7 x 4	14	1 x 7
7 x 5	21	4 x 7
7 x 2	28	2 x 7
7 x 3	35	5 x 7
7 x 6	42	7 x 7
7 x 8	49	6 x 7
7 x 10	56	8 x 7
7 x 7	63	12 x 7
7 x 12	70	9 x 7
7 x 9	77	11 x 7
7 x 11	84	10 x 7

Factors	Product	Factors
9 x 3	9	3 x 9
9 x 1	18	5 x 9
9 x 4	27	2 x 9
9 x 2	36	6 x 9
9 x 8	45	7 x 9
9 x 6	54	1 x 9
9 x 5	63	8 x 9
9 x 7	72	10 x 9
9 x 9	81	12 x 9
9 x 12	90	4 x 9
9 x 11	99	9 x 9
9 x 10	108	11 x 9

Multiply.

1 x 7	9 x 8	7 x 5	3 x 7	6 x 9	10 x 9	7 x 11	9 x 2
7 x 7	9 x 9	6 x 9	4 x 7	9 x 1	3 x 9	7 x 10	2 x 7
9 x 12	7 x 9	4 x 9	8 x 7	7 x 6	12 x 7	11 x 7	5 x 7

Multiply by 8
Concept & Commutative

8 dozen eggs
x 12 eggs per dozen

12 eggs per dozen, 8 dozen eggs
12 x 8 = _____

Multiply.

8 x 1	1 x 8	8 x 2	2 x 8
8 x 3	3 x 8	8 x 4	4 x 8
8 x 5	5 x 8	8 x 6	6 x 8
8 x 7	7 x 8	8 x 8	8 x 8
8 x 9	9 x 8	8 x 10	10 x 8
8 x 11	11 x 8	8 x 12	12 x 8

Write all the 8 times tables and their commutative partners.

8 x 1 = 8   1 x 8 = 8

51

Day 8 Wrap-Ups and Rapid Writing

Do the x8 Wrap-Up™ 5 times. Mark an X in the box each time you finish.

1. Write the answers to the problems in the first column as fast as you can.
2. Do the x8 Learning Wrap-Up™ until you meet your goal. Mark a box in the Keeping Track section each time you complete the Wrap-Up™.
3. Write the answers to the second and third columns as fast as you can.

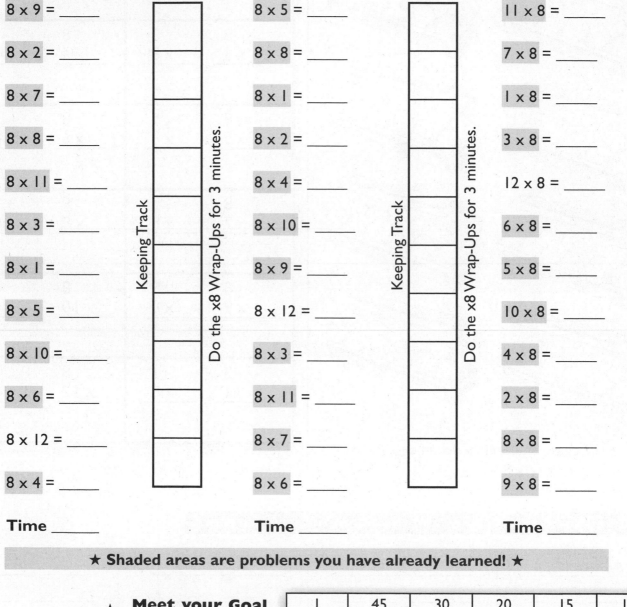

8 x 9 = _____

8 x 2 = _____

8 x 7 = _____

8 x 8 = _____

8 x 11 = _____

8 x 3 = _____

8 x 1 = _____

8 x 5 = _____

8 x 10 = _____

8 x 6 = _____

8 x 12 = _____

8 x 4 = _____

Time _____

Keeping Track

Do the x8 Wrap-Ups for 3 minutes.

8 x 5 = _____

8 x 8 = _____

8 x 1 = _____

8 x 2 = _____

8 x 4 = _____

8 x 10 = _____

8 x 9 = _____

8 x 12 = _____

8 x 3 = _____

8 x 11 = _____

8 x 7 = _____

8 x 6 = _____

Time _____

Keeping Track

Do the x8 Wrap-Ups for 3 minutes.

11 x 8 = _____

7 x 8 = _____

1 x 8 = _____

3 x 8 = _____

12 x 8 = _____

6 x 8 = _____

5 x 8 = _____

10 x 8 = _____

4 x 8 = _____

2 x 8 = _____

8 x 8 = _____

9 x 8 = _____

Time _____

★ Shaded areas are problems you have already learned! ★

★ **Meet your Goal**
Do the x8 Wrap-Up™ until you meet your goal.

1 minute	45 seconds	30 seconds	20 seconds	15 seconds	10 seconds
Getting started!	First goal. Keep going!	Champ!	Super Champ!	Awesome!	Next to impossible!

52

Day 8 Story Problems

Write an equation and a product to solve each problem.

---

1. Matt can see 7 rows of bricks on one side of the flagpole base. Each row has 8 bricks. Draw the bricks. Write the equation and product.

_____ x _____ = _____

---

2. Ron went to the egg farm on a field trip. He noticed 8 small egg cartons that held only 6 eggs. Draw a picture of the eggs in the cartons. Write the equation and product.

_____ x _____ = _____

---

3. Rich put jelly beans on a paper. He put 8 jelly beans in a row. There were 6 rows. Draw the jelly beans. Write the equation and product.

_____ x _____ = _____

---

4. Tasha carried a tray of empty milk cartons to the art room. There were 3 rows of cartons. There were 8 cartons in each row. How many cartons were there? Write the equation and the product.

_____ x _____ = _____

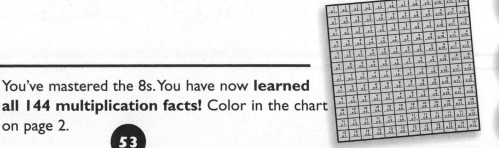

★ **CONGRATULATIONS!** You've mastered the 8s. You have now **learned all 144 multiplication facts!** Color in the chart on page 2.

Start at the top and make a trail with your pencil through the x8 number family. Each time you get to 96, start over with 8. Can you get to the end without lifting your pencil off the paper?

Cover the skip counting numbers on the left side of the page, then write all the x8 family numbers you can remember. Two of them are done.

Start →

8	32	40	48	56	64
16	24	96	88	80	72
56	48	8			
64	40	16			
72	32	24			
80	88	96			
56	48	8			
64	40	16			
72	32	24			
80	40	48			
88	32	56			
96	24	64			
8	16	72			
96	88	80			

End ←

8

96

Cross out the numbers that are not part of the x8 family.

8 40 24 96 82 80 48 32 64
58
72 80 68 16 72 88 56 13 42
64
96 56 24 32 40 86 48 16 88
58
8 32 62 18 42

Column 1	Column 2	Column 3	Column 4
5 x 2 = _____	4 x 3 = _____	3 x 4 = _____	5 x 12 = _____
1 x 2 = _____	9 x 3 = _____	7 x 4 = _____	5 x 4 = _____
6 x 2 = _____	1 x 3 = _____	9 x 4 = _____	5 x 2 = _____
8 x 2 = _____	8 x 3 = _____	4 x 4 = _____	5 x 5 = _____
12 x 2 = _____	5 x 3 = _____	12 x 4 = _____	5 x 7 = _____
3 x 2 = _____	10 x 3 = _____	5 x 4 = _____	5 x 1 = _____
4 x 2 = _____	7 x 3 = _____	6 x 4 = _____	5 x 8 = _____
2 x 2 = _____	12 x 3 = _____	11 x 4 = _____	5 x 9 = _____
10 x 2 = _____	2 x 3 = _____	8 x 4 = _____	5 x 3 = _____
7 x 2 = _____	11 x 3 = _____	1 x 4 = _____	5 x 6 = _____
11 x 2 = _____	6 x 3 = _____	10 x 4 = _____	5 x 10 = _____
9 x 2 = _____	3 x 3 = _____	2 x 4 = _____	5 x 11 = _____

Column 5	Column 6	Column 7	Column 8
5 x 6 = _____	4 x 7 = _____	8 x 8 = _____	9 x 12 = _____
1 x 6 = _____	3 x 7 = _____	7 x 8 = _____	9 x 4 = _____
6 x 6 = _____	1 x 7 = _____	10 x 8 = _____	9 x 2 = _____
9 x 6 = _____	8 x 7 = _____	4 x 8 = _____	9 x 5 = _____
12 x 6 = _____	5 x 7 = _____	12 x 8 = _____	9 x 7 = _____
3 x 6 = _____	10 x 7 = _____	5 x 8 = _____	9 x 1 = _____
4 x 6 = _____	7 x 7 = _____	6 x 8 = _____	9 x 8 = _____
2 x 6 = _____	12 x 7 = _____	11 x 8 = _____	9 x 9 = _____
10 x 6 = _____	2 x 7 = _____	3 x 8 = _____	9 x 3 = _____
7 x 6 = _____	11 x 7 = _____	1 x 8 = _____	9 x 6 = _____
11 x 6 = _____	6 x 7 = _____	2 x 8 = _____	9 x 10 = _____
8 x 6 = _____	9 x 7 = _____	9 x 8 = _____	9 x 11 = _____

My Wrap-Ups™ Journal

Write about something you learned, something you are having trouble learning, or something interesting you discovered about multiplication today.

Date _____

_____

_____

_____

Date _____

_____

_____

_____

Date _____

_____

_____

_____

My Wrap-Ups™ Journal

Date _____

_____

_____

_____

Date _____

_____

_____

_____

Date _____

_____

_____

_____

My Wrap-Ups™ Journal

Date _____

_____

_____

_____

Date _____

_____

_____

_____

Date _____

_____

_____

_____

My Wrap-Ups™ Journal

Date _____

_____

_____

_____

_____

Date _____

_____

_____

_____

_____

Date _____

_____

_____

_____

_____

My Wrap-Ups™ Journal

Date _____

_____

_____

_____

_____

Date _____

_____

_____

_____

_____

Date _____

_____

_____

_____

_____

My Wrap-Ups™ Multiplication Glossary

column

a vertical (up and down) group

commutative property of multiplication

The order of numbers in a multiplication problem can change and the product will stay the same.

digit

one of the numerals in a number

equation

a number sentence

factor

one of the numbers multiplied together in a multiplication problem

perfect square

a multiplication equation in which the two factors are the same

product

the answer in a multiplication problem

row

a horizontal (side to side) group